THE BIBLE STORY

VOLUME IX

—————•◆•—————

KING OF KINGS

(From the Closing Scenes of Jesus' Life to His Ascension)

The
BIBLE STORY

More Than Four Hundred Stories in Ten Volumes
Covering the Entire Bible From Genesis to Revelation

VOLUME NINE
King of Kings

BY ARTHUR S. MAXWELL

Author of *Uncle Arthur's Bedtime Stories, The Children's Hour With Uncle Arthur,*
The Secret of the Cave, etc.

•

REVIEW AND HERALD PUBLISHING ASSOCIATION
Washington, D.C.

CONTENTS

Part I—Stories of the King of Lovers

MATTHEW 16:21-23; 18:1-19:30; 21:12-16; 26:6-13; MARK 10:13-11:19; 12:20-33; 14:3-11; LUKE 7:36-50; 9:51-56; 18:15-19:48; JOHN 11:55-12:33

Part II—Stories of the King of Sorrows

MATTHEW 26:20-75; MARK 14:12-15:20; LUKE 22:3-46; JOHN 11:27-57; 13:1-18:37

5

Hearing of the cruel death of Jesus, the children who loved Him must have been broken-hearted to find only an empty cross, the crown of thorns, and a few nails to tell the story.

Part III—*Stories of the King of Sufferers*

Matthew 27:20-66; Mark 15:21-47; Luke 23:18-56; John 19:1-42

Part IV—*Stories of the King of Life*

Matthew 28:1-20; Mark 16:1-20; Luke 24:1-53; John 20:1-21:25; Acts 1:1-11

PART I

Stories of the King of Lovers

(MATTHEW 16:21-23; 18:1-19:30; 21:12-16; 26:6-13; MARK 10: 13-11:19; 12:20-33; 14:3-11; LUKE 7:36-50; 9:51-56; 18:15-19: 48; JOHN 11:55-12:33)

≈≈≈≈≈≈≈≈≈≈≈

STORY 1

Friend of Children

≈≈≈≈≈≈≈≈≈≈≈≈≈≈≈≈≈≈≈≈≈≈≈≈≈

HE MAY have been four. He may have been five. I don't know. Nobody knows.

His name may have been Amos, or Enoch, or Benjamin. Again I don't know. Nobody knows.

But for one brief hour he was the most favored boy in all the world. Jesus picked him out of a crowd of children and told everybody around to become like this little boy or they would never enter His kingdom of love.

What a dear, sweet boy he must have been! So kind, loving, and obedient! The goodness in his heart must have been shining from his face, and Jesus saw it.

He couldn't have been one of the rough kind, rushing around shouting and whistling and making a nuisance of himself. He couldn't have been shoving the other boys about or teasing the little girls and making them cry. No. He was just standing there quietly and respectfully, looking up at Jesus with wide-open eyes, watching everything He did and listen-

9

← PAINTING BY HARRY ANDERSON   © 1957, BY REVIEW AND HERALD

Jesus loved children. Their simplicity, their trust, their simple faith were qualities that made them dear to the heart of God. It is with childlike faith He wishes us to come to Him.

ing to every word He said, so happy to be near Jesus. Then he heard his name called.

The Bible says, "Jesus called a little child unto Him."

"John," He said—and the boy's name could have been John, couldn't it? "Please come here a moment. I need you."

Little John, blushing and smiling, ran toward the Master, while all the other children pressed near to see what would happen next.

Then, perhaps with one hand placed gently on little John's head, Jesus said to the grownups who were listening to Him, "Unless you turn and become like children, you will never enter the kingdom of heaven."

His disciples had just asked Him who would be the greatest in His kingdom, and this was His answer. The kingdom of heaven is for the humble, the gentle, the kind, the unselfish. Unless the disciples stopped wanting the best things and the best places for themselves they would never see heaven.

"Whoever humbles himself like this child," Jesus said, "he is the greatest in the kingdom of heaven."

Then Jesus went on to say something else that was on His heart. And there was sternness in His voice as He warned the grownups never to lead a child into sin. Should anyone do so, He said, "it would be better for him to have a great millstone fastened round his neck and to be drowned in the depth of the sea."

At this, little John and the other children must have thought, "How wonderful to have Somebody to care for us like this! Why, not only is Jesus our friend; He's our own big brother!"

They became more sure of this as Jesus went on to say to the grownups, "See that you do not despise one of these little ones; for I tell you that in heaven their angels always behold the face of My Father who is in heaven." Then He added, "It is not the will of My Father who is in heaven that one of these little ones should perish."

How dearly Jesus must love children! Nothing happens to any boy or girl in all the world but it is known to Him and the angels. If anyone starts bullying one of His "little ones," or tempting him to do wrong, he had better look out! Jesus will deal with him like the wonderful big brother that He is!

You can imagine how the children, hearing Jesus say such things, came to love Him more and more. He was their hero. They were ready to do anything He said and follow Him anywhere He went.

Mothers loved Him too, because He loved their children. They brought their babies to Him and begged Him just to put His hands on them and bless them.

The Bible tells of one such happy scene. Boys and girls were crowding around Jesus as usual. There was much fun and innocent laughter as there always is when children get together. Then mothers began to come with their little ones in their arms.

"Bless my little Jacob!" I can hear one saying.

"And my little Rebekah!" said another.

"And my precious Daniel! Please, Jesus, put your hands on him!"

Jesus smiled as He cuddled the babies in His arms, whispering gently to one after another, "Bless you, darling! Bless you, little sweetheart!"

To the mothers I am sure He said, "And mind you bring them up right. Be sure to teach them to love God and keep His commandments."

FRIEND OF CHILDREN

Then suddenly somebody spoiled it all.

"Get away, get away!" one of the disciples was saying. "Leave the Master alone! Can't you see He's tired? He has more important things to do than bless your children. Get away!"

Hurt and disappointed, the mothers and children looked around, wondering what they had done wrong. Maybe some of them started to go away. Then Jesus spoke up. He told them to stay, and rebuked the disciples for acting like this.

"Suffer little children, and forbid them not, to come unto Me: for of such is the kingdom of heaven," He said.

"Let the children alone, do not stop them from coming to Me," is the way another translation reads.

What a nice, kind thing for Him to say!

And He hasn't changed a bit since then. He said it on that far-off afternoon. He says it now today. "Don't stop the children coming to Me!" He wants every boy and girl in all the world to come to Him. No matter where you live, or how you dress, or what language you speak, His invitation is to you. Just come. And you may be sure He will never turn any child away.

But what did Jesus mean when He said, "Of such is the kingdom of heaven"? Are all children ready for heaven? Oh, no indeed. I can think of some who are so naughty and rude and disobedient they would turn heaven into a madhouse if they should ever get there. Others are so destructive they would tear the New Jerusalem to pieces in no time at all if Jesus were to let them in.

Jesus was thinking of sweet, innocent, unspoiled children when He said, "Of such is the kingdom of heaven." He had in mind those dear boys and girls who respect and obey their parents and who try to be helpful and unselfish at home and at school. Heaven will be made up of people like this.

And if we are not like this now? Then we must change, or be left out. That is why Jesus wants us to come to Him, so He can change us.

He wants to make us as kind, patient, tender-hearted, and sweet-tempered as He was as a boy.

STORY 2

Youth Jesus Loved

HOW LONG Jesus spent with the boys and girls and babies that happy afternoon I do not know. At last, however, He told them it was time for them all to go home to supper and to bed.

"Good-by, Jesus, good-by, good-by!" I can hear them calling as they slowly walked away.

Perhaps Jesus said to Himself, "What dear children! How I love them! And now I'll have a little peace and quiet for a while." But it was not to be. For just then a young man came running toward Him.

Such a noble-looking lad he was—big, strong, and clean—his fine clothes telling that he belonged to the wealthy class. Nobody quite like this had ever come to Jesus before, and the Lord was glad to see him.

"Good Master," said the youth, kneeling respectfully, "what shall I do that I may inherit eternal life?"

It was a thoughtful question and showed that the young

15

man had been thinking seriously about the future. People had told him that Jesus was preaching about a kingdom in which there would be no death and where everybody would live forever, and he had come to find out how he could share in it.

Looking tenderly into the young man's earnest, upturned face, Jesus said, "You know the commandments: Do not commit adultery, Do not kill, Do not steal, Do not bear false witness, Defraud not, Honor thy father and mother."

"Master," replied the youth eagerly, "all these have I observed from my youth."

Clearly this fine lad loved God and wanted to do right. As a child he had memorized the Ten Commandments, and he still knew them by heart. They were the guiding rules of his life.

No wonder that "Jesus beholding him loved him."

Jesus saw all the good in him and all the good he might do in days to come. This noble youth could become a great church leader, a mighty champion of His kingdom of love.

"You lack one thing," said Jesus.

"Just one thing!" I can hear the young man saying. "Only one! What is it, Lord? Tell me and I will do it! Anything, anything, for the rich boon of eternal life."

"I'll tell you," said Jesus. "If you want to be perfect, sell everything you have and give to the poor, and you will have treasure in heaven. Then come, take up the cross, and follow me."

Joy left the young man's face, as though a light had gone out inside him.

9-2

17

A rich young ruler, who said he had always kept the commandments, respectfully came to Jesus and sincerely asked, "Good Master, what shall I do that I may inherit eternal life?"

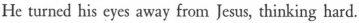

He turned his eyes away from Jesus, thinking hard.

Was this the price of eternal life? Must he sell his property and give away everything he owned to the poor? Must he become like those Galilean fishermen and live in poverty the rest of his life? He couldn't do it. It was asking too much.

For a moment there must have been an awful silence as the young man made up his mind. Then, without another word, he slowly turned and "went away sorrowful: for he had great possessions."

Jesus must have been sorry too. Perhaps He longed to call the young man back and make things easier for him. But He didn't. He saw that this youth's great lack was sympathy for others. He wanted eternal life for himself but not for the sad and hungry about him. He had tried to keep the Ten Commandments exactly as they were written, but he had failed to see that what God wants most is a loving heart moved with compassion for those in need.

But before you blame this youth for what he did, think about yourself. Jesus, beholding you, loves you. But perhaps He is saying to you right now, "You lack one thing."

It could be unselfishness. It could be a forgiving spirit. It could be gentleness or politeness. It could be respect for your parents. It could be one of many things. But you had better find out what it is. For that one thing could keep you out of heaven. It could rob you of eternal life.

And when Jesus points it out, don't go away sorrowful. Instead, kneel before Him and say, "Dear Lord, supply the thing I lack. Make me perfect in Thee."

18

STORY 3

Village Jesus Wouldn't Burn

≈≈≈≈≈≈≈≈≈≈≈≈≈≈≈≈≈≈≈≈≈≈≈≈≈≈≈≈≈≈

TIME was running out for Jesus, and He knew it. When He was alone with His disciples He tried to tell them that the happy, carefree days would soon be over, but they wouldn't believe Him.

He told them "that He must go unto Jerusalem, and suffer many things of the elders and chief priests and scribes, and be killed, and be raised again the third day," but it all seemed impossible to them. Peter even began to rebuke Him, saying, "Be it far from Thee, Lord: this shall not be unto Thee."

Everything had gone so well up to now. The miracles of healing. The crowds that came to listen. The feeding of the five thousand. What a wonderful time it had been! Surely Jesus wouldn't let a few priests and scribes spoil His plans to set up His glorious kingdom.

Somehow it hadn't dawned on them yet that if Jesus was indeed the Lamb of God, as John the Baptist had said, He must someday be offered up as a sacrifice. That was something

19

beyond their imagination, and too terrible to think about.

But Jesus thought about it. And as day followed day the shadows of the cross began to gather about Him.

It would have been so easy to run away and hide somewhere. He could have gone to India, or China, or Africa, and nobody would have found Him there. But He didn't run away, even though He knew all about the terrible things that were going to happen to Him. Instead, "He stedfastly set His face to go to Jerusalem." That must have taken a lot of courage.

And it was just then that something very beautiful happened.

Evening was approaching, and Jesus had sent James and John ahead to look for lodgings for the night.

The nearest village belonged to the Samaritans, but this did not worry the two disciples. Had not Jesus been especially kind to Samaritans so they would see that He loved them as much as He loved the Jews? Had He not spent several wonderful days in Sychar healing all their sick?

But when the disciples asked for rooms they were refused.

"But why?" they asked. "Why?"

"Because your Master is on His way to Jerusalem."

It was a foolish reason. So little, so childish.

James and John became so angry they said to Jesus, "Would you like us to command fire to come down from heaven and consume them, as Elijah did?"

Jesus was shocked. What a dreadful thing to suggest to the King of lovers! To think that His disciples would talk like this after living with Him for three years! Didn't they

20

understand yet that He had come from heaven to reveal the love of God to men?

In words that will never die He said, "The Son of man is not come to destroy men's lives, but to save them."

Looking at the little village that had refused Him shelter, He felt only pity for the people who lived there. Poor things! They didn't know any better. How *could* they know that He was on His way to Jerusalem to die for them as well as for everybody else in the world? Someday they would see how they had missed their chance to welcome the Son of God and cheer His heart before His great sorrow. But not now. Their shriveled hearts were too full of petty jealousies. It was too bad. But Jesus would not let Himself be angry with them. He had come to save, not to destroy.

"And they went to another village."

We don't know which one it was, but it was blessed with the presence of the Saviour. The people there gained what the others lost.

STORY 4

Tears Jesus Shed

ONE DAY a messenger came to Jesus, bringing news from Mary and Martha in Bethany.

The message was very short, just like a telegram: "Lord, he whom You love is ill."

That was all. It didn't even say, "Please come at once." The two sisters were so sure Jesus would come as soon as He could.

But He didn't go at once. In fact He didn't do anything about it. Not that He wasn't sorry for Lazarus, Mary, and Martha. No indeed, for the Bible says that He loved them. Then why did He stay around for two days before leaving?

That's what the disciples wanted to know. But all He would say was that this illness of Lazarus was for the glory of God.

By and by Jesus said, "Our friend Lazarus sleepeth."

"That's fine," said the disciples. "If he has gone to sleep, he will get better."

TEARS JESUS SHED

Then Jesus told them plainly that Lazarus was dead. He had used the word "sleep" because that is what death really is. It's just like going to bed at night and not waking up till someone calls you in the morning.

Now they started off for Bethany, the disciples wondering how Jesus knew Lazarus was dead and whether they would be in time for the funeral.

They weren't. Jesus did not seem to be in the least bit of a hurry, and when they arrived in Bethany they found that Lazarus had been buried four days already.

"Lord," said Martha, "if You had been here, my brother would not have died."

No doubt she was right. And she couldn't understand why Jesus had not come when she sent for Him. But now she said something that pleased Jesus very much.

"Even now I know that whatever You ask from God, God will give You."

This showed that, even though she was the busy one about the house, "cumbered about much serving," she loved and trusted Jesus just as much as Mary.

"Your brother will rise again," Jesus said tenderly.

"I know that he will rise again in the resurrection at the last day," Martha replied.

"I am the resurrection and the life," said Jesus, in one of the most glorious statements He ever made; "he who believes in Me, though he die, yet shall he live, and whoever lives and believes in Me shall never die. Do you believe this?"

"Yes, Lord," said Martha; "I believe that You are the

Christ, the Son of God." What a wonderful confession!

"Where's Mary?" asked Jesus.

Martha went to the house and found her sister in the midst of many mourners, who were trying to comfort her.

"The Master is here," whispered Martha; "He is calling for you."

Silently Mary rose and went with her sister.

Thinking that the two women were going to the tomb to weep, the mourners followed them.

It was a sad, sad procession. Mary was weeping bitterly, and the others were crying with her.

Then Mary caught sight of Jesus. "Lord," she sobbed, "if You had been here, my brother would not have died."

He didn't try to explain.

"Where have you laid him?" He asked gently.

"Come and see," she said.

So they went to the tomb.

Everybody was weeping now. Jesus cried too. The Bible says so in those two most precious words: "Jesus wept."

Great tears rolled down the cheeks of the King of lovers as He cried in sympathy for the brokenhearted people.

"See how He loved him!" some of the onlookers said.

Yes, indeed. And they might have said, "See how He loves everybody!" For it was not for Mary and Martha alone that He wept that day, but for all who mourn in every age—young and old, rich and poor, in all the wide, wide world.

Those tears of Jesus tell us how much He cares for us. If you are feeling sad and lonely just now, think about them.

They will comfort you, for His great heart of love is still touched with our griefs.

Coming to the tomb, which was a cave with a large stone rolled in front of it, the mourners stood still, wondering what Jesus was going to do.

"Roll away the stone!" He commanded.

The mourners were horrified.

Martha, ever practical, urged Him not to do it. "He has been dead four days," she said; and she meant that his body had already begun to decay.

Perceiving their unbelief, Jesus answered with a note of authority in His voice, "Did I not tell you that if you would believe you would see the glory of God?"

The stone was taken away.

Then Jesus began to pray.

"Father, I thank Thee that Thou hast heard Me," He said, as though He had been praying about this for some time.

Then He went on. "I knew that Thou hearest Me always, but I have said this on account of the people standing by, that they may believe that Thou didst send Me."

By this time a great silence had fallen upon the crowd. Everyone had ceased sobbing. They were all now anxiously looking at Jesus.

What was He planning to do? Surely He was not going to try to bring a man back to life who had been dead four days!

Suddenly, Jesus commanded, "Lazarus, come out!"

All eyes turned toward the mouth of the cave.

There was a rustling sound within. Something, somebody, was moving about inside! Surely, it could not be—but it was.

A moment later Lazarus appeared. He was a shocking sight, for a cloth was wrapped about his face, and his hands and feet were still bound in the bandages that undertakers wound around the dead in those days.

How he reached the mouth of the cave like that is a mystery, but there he was and the people gasped in awe.

"Unbind him, and let him go," said Jesus, and they did.

Then what a joyous scene took place! I imagine Lazarus threw his arms about Mary and Martha and kissed them. Then he shook hands with all his old friends who had never dreamed they would see him alive again.

Maybe they felt him all over to make sure he was real. He was. Perhaps they asked him what it felt like to be dead, but he couldn't remember anything. "It was just like being fast asleep," he told them.

Thus did Jesus again turn sorrow into joy, and tears to smiles of happiness.

By and by Mary and Martha looked around to thank Him for all He had done for them. But He was nowhere to be seen. He had just walked quietly away.

PAINTING BY WILLIAM HUTCHINSON

STORY 5

Secret Jesus Told

IN ALMOST no time at all after Lazarus stepped out of his tomb all Jerusalem knew about it. The news spread like wildfire.

Many Jews had gone to Bethany for his funeral. Now they heard that the man they had seen buried was alive. Jesus, the preacher from Galilee, had brought him back from the dead! It was by far the biggest news to hit the city in many a long day.

The common people were thrilled. It made them more sure than ever that Jesus was their long-hoped-for Messiah. But the priests and rulers were much upset. Such a miracle, they knew, would turn the hearts of all Israel to this man who was breaking down all their traditions. In their anger some of them began to suggest that there would be trouble with the Romans if Jesus wasn't stopped before He went any further. Caiaphas the high priest even said it might be wise to have Him arrested and put to death.

SECRET JESUS TOLD

Never had the old city of David been so stirred.

Meanwhile, in Bethany, a Pharisee called Simon was putting on a big party, with Jesus and Lazarus as the guests of honor. Jesus had once healed Simon of leprosy. That's why he was so friendly.

The house was full of guests, including Mary and Martha and many of the disciples. When suppertime came "Martha served" as usual. She couldn't help it—and they couldn't get on without her. Mary, however, had no liking for such things; she was thinking of Jesus and how much He had done for her. In a way she too had been raised from the dead. Had He not saved her from a very wicked life?

She longed to tell Him how grateful she was and how much she loved Him. But how?

She had an idea—but dare she act on it? She had thought about it a long time and saved up for it, and—well, maybe *now* was the time. After all, He wouldn't be here much longer if the wicked rulers in Jerusalem had their way with Him.

Slowly she walked toward Jesus, unnoticed by the guests, who were busily eating and chatting with one another. From

beneath some covering, maybe the folds of her skirt, she brought a lovely alabaster jar, full of expensive perfume. Quickly she poured some of it on the head and feet of her beloved Master.

At once everybody paused, sniffing. "What has happened?" they asked, recognizing the agreeable aroma. Then they turned toward Jesus, where Mary, weeping hard, was wiping His feet with her long, beautiful hair.

For a moment everyone was struck dumb. Nobody could think of anything to say. Then Judas, who looked after the disciples' moneybag, blurted out, "Why this waste? Why was not this perfume sold and the money given to the poor?" Not that he cared for the poor, of course. It was just to make the others think he was pious. But he made a mistake.

"Why do you trouble the woman?" said Jesus. "For she

has done a beautiful thing to Me. For you always have the poor with you, but you will not always have Me. In pouring this ointment on My body she has done it to prepare Me for burial."

Then He made a remarkable prophecy.

"Truly, I say to you, wherever this gospel is preached in the whole world, what she has done will be told in memory of her."

And so it has happened through all the nineteen hundred years that have passed since then. Mary's lovely deed will never be forgotten.

But Simon was troubled. He knew Mary well. He had known her when she was a very bad girl, and he couldn't understand why Jesus would let a woman with such a past behave like this.

He thought to himself, "If this man were a prophet, He would have known who and what sort of woman this is who is touching Him, for she is a sinner."

Jesus read his thoughts.

"Simon," He said, "I have something to say to you."

"What is it?" asked Simon.

Then Jesus told him a story about a man who was owed money by two people. One owed five hundred pence, the other fifty. Seeing they had nothing with which to pay, the man forgave them both.

"Tell me," said Jesus, "which will love him most?"

"The one who was forgiven most," said Simon.

"Right!" said Jesus.

Then, pointing to Mary, He said, "Do you see this woman? I entered your house, you gave Me no water for My feet, but she has wet My feet with her tears and wiped them with her hair. You gave Me no kiss, but from the time I came in she has not ceased to kiss My feet. You did not anoint My head with oil, but she has anointed My feet with ointment. Therefore I tell you, her sins, which are many, are forgiven, for she loved much; but he who is forgiven little, loves little."

Then, speaking to Mary, He said, "Your sins are forgiven. . . . Your faith has saved you; go in peace."

Simon was shocked.

He had thought that because Mary had once been a sinner she must always be a sinner. Now Jesus said that it wasn't so. Mary was no longer a sinner in the eyes of God. She had been forgiven. Her sins, all of them, bad as they were, had been wiped away. She was as dear to God as if she had never sinned. She was His child, now and forever.

This was the secret Jesus told; the glorious secret of redeeming love.

STORY 6

Donkey Jesus Remembered

FOR A LITTLE while Jesus kept out of sight in the village of Ephraim "near to the wilderness." By so doing He avoided the priests and rulers who had now made up their minds to get rid of Him.

Then, as the Passover drew near, He set out once more for Jerusalem.

The road took Him through dear old Bethany to the Mount of Olives. Here He stopped and surprised His disciples by asking two of them to do a very strange thing.

They were to go into a nearby village and borrow a donkey!

Jesus knew exactly where it was, just inside the gate.

He also knew the donkey's age; it was so young no one had sat upon it yet.

It could well be that He had seen this fine little animal the last time He passed this way, and now that He needed a donkey He remembered it.

"Untie it," He said, "and bring it here."

9-3

Naturally the disciples wondered what the owner would say. Jesus knew their thoughts and said, "If anyone asks you, 'Why are you untying it?' you shall say this, 'The Lord has need of it.'"

Still wondering why Jesus should want a donkey, the disciples walked over to the village. There, just where Jesus had told them, they found the young colt and untied it.

As they were doing so the owners came up and asked, "Why are you untying the colt?"

"The Lord has need of it," they said, and took it away. Perhaps the owners were believers in Jesus and were glad to lend Him their animal.

When the disciples returned with the donkey Jesus must have told them what He was going to do with it. The time had come when the prophecy of Zechariah 9:9 was to be fulfilled: "Rejoice greatly, O daughter of Zion; shout, O daughter of Jerusalem: behold, thy King cometh unto thee: He is just, and having salvation; lowly, and riding upon an ass, and upon a colt the foal of an ass."

Suddenly a great hope rose in the hearts of the disciples. Could this be the moment they had been waiting for? Was

34

Jesus going to let Himself be crowned king of Israel after all? How wonderful! How glorious!

They had no cloth of gold to put on the donkey's back, but each one of them gladly offered a garment to make it look as fancy as possible. Then "they set Jesus upon it."

What pride and joy welled up in their hearts as they saw Him sitting there! True, He didn't look much like a king. He wore no jeweled crown or royal robes. Yet there was something about His face that made Him more than kingly. It was the kindness, goodness, and strength of character shining there.

Suddenly the donkey took a step forward. Someone shouted, "Blessed be the King who comes in the name of the Lord!" and others took up the cry. Soon everybody around was shouting, "Blessed be the King who comes in the name of the Lord! Peace in heaven and glory in the highest!"

Every moment excitement grew. People came running from all directions to find out what was going on.

"What's happening?" they cried. "What's going on here?"

"It's Jesus of Nazareth, the great teacher of Galilee. He's going to Jerusalem to be crowned king of Israel. Can't you see He's riding on a donkey, just as the prophet said?"

Then more and more people joined in the shouting, "Blessed be the King who comes in the name of the Lord."

Boys and girls rushed to join the procession, their eyes alight with gladness. This was their day. Now they could let everybody know how much they loved the man who had been so kind and gentle to them. At the top of their voices they shouted, "Hosanna to the Son of David!"

As Jesus rode slowly on His way the crowd became denser than ever. The Bible says, "Most of the crowd spread their garments before Him in the road; and others cut branches from the trees and spread them on the road.

"And the crowds that went before Him and that followed Him shouted, 'Hosanna to the Son of David! Blessed be He who comes in the name of the Lord! Hosanna in the highest!'"

Now some of the priests and rulers came on the scene. They were not pleased. Those who managed to get close to Jesus said, "Master, rebuke Your disciples!" But He answered,

"If these should hold their peace, the stones would immediately cry out."

By this He meant that the prophecy of Zechariah must be fulfilled. The time had come for this to happen, and nobody on earth could stop it.

As the procession neared Jerusalem "all the city was moved, saying, Who is this? And the multitude said, This is Jesus the prophet of Nazareth of Galilee."

It was indeed. Only He was more than a prophet. He was a king. Their king. The King of Israel. The King of the world.

The King of kings. And He was riding on His royal way to the city of David. What a pity everybody did not receive Him gladly! How different all history might have been!

But it was a great day for the disciples—their last happy day before the cross.

It was a great day also for all the boys and girls who followed Him. Never would they forget the thrill of that wonderful procession.

And it was a great day too for that little donkey. In his wildest dreams—if donkeys ever dream—he never thought he might carry his Creator on the day of His triumph. If donkeys think, he may have thought, "The Lord could have chosen a lion, an elephant, or a beautiful Arabian horse for such a wonderful occasion as this, but instead He chose me, a little donkey!"

And what was it that the two disciples said as they went to untie the donkey? "The Lord has need of it."

Yes; He had need of this humble little animal to fulfill a great prophecy on one of the greatest days of His life.

What a lesson for us all! It could be that we—you and I—are like that little donkey, just standing around with nothing much to do, perhaps thinking that nobody cares for us. But Jesus cares. He remembers us. He knows where we are. And He has need of us. Today, in what may be history's greatest hour, He has something for all of us to do for Him.

A lovely little prayer would be, "Lord, if Thou needest me, show me how, and where, and when. Help me to do my best for Thee. Use me as Thou wilt—all the way to the New Jerusalem."

38

STORY 7

The King Who Stopped
to Cry

WHAT a procession that was! There had never been anything like it in all the history of the world. True, many kings had ridden in triumph but never one without a soldier or a weapon or a flag.

Many a king had gloried in the prisoners that followed him, bound with chains; but this King rejoiced that all in His procession were bound by bonds of love alone.

Nobody here had been forced into service or struck in anger. The followers of this Conqueror had felt nothing but the gentle touch of His loving hand.

Nobody here had had his eyes put out, or his back beaten with rods, or his feet crushed in the stocks. Instead, here were the blind to whom this King had given sight, the deaf to whom He had given hearing, the lame whom He had made to walk, lepers whom He had cleansed, and at least one whom He had brought back from the grave.

No wonder there was so much cheering! No wonder

39

everybody was shouting, "Blessed be the King who comes in the name of the Lord!"

Then to everybody's surprise the procession stopped. Those who were ahead no doubt walked on some distance before discovering that Jesus wasn't with them any more. Hurriedly turning back to see what had gone wrong, they found a great crowd of people gathered very closely around the Saviour.

Here indeed was a strange sight. Jesus had stopped His donkey at a high point on the road from which Jerusalem could be clearly seen. He was looking at the city and seemed to be talking to it. Yes, and, of all things, He was crying! Tears were coursing down His cheeks.

Whatever could be the matter? Whoever heard of a king crying when everyone was shouting his praise?

Those nearest to Jesus pressed closer to catch His words.

"If thou hadst known," Jesus was saying, His lips quivering, "even thou, at least in this thy day, the things which belong unto thy peace! But now they are hid from thine eyes.

40

PAINTING BY HERBERT RUDEEN

THE KING WHO STOPPED TO CRY

"For the days shall come upon thee, that thine enemies shall cast a trench about thee, and compass thee round, and keep thee in on every side, and shall lay thee even with the ground, and thy children within thee; and they shall not leave in thee one stone upon another; because thou knewest not the time of thy visitation." Thus He forecast the city's doom.

What words for a king to say to his own city! But this

was no ordinary king, full of pride and vainglory. This was the King of lovers who was about to be rejected by the very people He loved so much. From where He stood He no doubt could see all the royal pomp and glitter of Herod's palace as well as the Praetorium where Pilate would release Him to the mob, the very buildings where the chief priests would scoff at Him, and where the Roman soldiers would mock Him and spit upon Him. And only a little way off, outside the city wall, was Calvary, or Golgotha, where they would crucify Him.

THE KING WHO STOPPED TO CRY

It was all so near now, so very near. Yet Jesus did not cry for Himself, but because of the poor people of the city who would suffer in years to come because they had not recognized their Messiah when He came to them.

From where Jesus sat upon the donkey's back, not only could He see the Temple and the royal palace and all the hundreds and hundreds of little homes about them; but looking into the future, He could see also the coming of the Roman armies to sack the city. He could see the soldiers storming the walls, setting fire to the buildings, putting thousands to death, and taking the rest into captivity.

"O Jerusalem, Jerusalem, thou that killest the prophets, and stonest them which are sent unto thee," He cried, "how often would I have gathered thy children together, even as a hen gathereth her chickens under her wings, and ye would not! Behold, your house is left unto you desolate!"

How much Jesus would have done for Jerusalem if only her people and her rulers had yielded themselves to His love and given their hearts to Him! It would have become the greatest and most beautiful city in all the world. It would have become known not only as the city of peace but as the city of light and the city of love. Peace, light, and love would have flowed from it, like streams of living water, to the ends of the earth.

It was a lovely dream, but it couldn't come true. The time had arrived but the people weren't ready. How terribly disappointing! How very, very sad!

No wonder the King of lovers cried.

STORY 8

Scene in the Temple

WHAT happened to the procession after that, we are not told. Perhaps at the sight of Jesus' tears the crowds scattered. I wouldn't be surprised if some of the people said, "What a strange sort of king, crying like that in public! Maybe he isn't a king after all."

They just didn't understand.

Anyway, as darkness fell they all went home to talk about the strange and wonderful day it had been.

Next morning Jesus appeared in the Temple, and soon things began to happen again.

Years before, at the beginning of His ministry, He had driven the merchants and money-changers out of this sacred place. Now He caught sight of them again. They were back in their old places, busy as ever.

Some were selling calves, some sheep, some pigeons, though the biggest business at this season of the year was in lambs for the Passover. Meanwhile, the money-changers were changing

44

SCENE IN THE TEMPLE

Greek and Roman coins for the "holy" money of the Temple —at a good profit, of course.

With all this buying and selling of animals, the place looked like a market and smelled like a farmyard.

To Jesus it was all wrong. How could people worship God properly with all this business going on? He longed to bear witness against it once more.

Advancing upon the money-changers, the pigeon sellers, and the rest of the merchants, He called out in a loud voice, "Take these things away! It is written, 'My house shall be called a house of prayer'; but you have made it a den of robbers!"

Seizing a table belonging to one of the money-changers, He tipped it over, scattering the silver coins all over the pavement. Then He moved to another and another and did the same. Coming to the seats of the pigeon sellers, He pushed them over also, repeating again and again, "Take these things away! My house shall be called a house of prayer."

The merchants and the money-changers were furious. They remembered how Jesus had done this once before and how

they had sworn vengeance on Him if He should ever do it again. But now that He was here they could do nothing. There was something about this Man of Nazareth that filled them with fear. They wanted to run from Him and hide.

Muttering threats, they knelt and picked up their scattered coins. Then they slunk away to the priests to tell them that they *must* do something about this Galilean or He'd turn the whole country upside down.

But the priests were helpless too. They just stood looking on with rising anger as more and more people, hearing what Jesus had done, flocked into the Temple to see the great sight.

Men and women, boys and girls, came hurrying by hundreds, all eager for the new excitement. And when the children caught sight of Jesus, again they began chanting, as they had the day before, "Hosanna to the son of David!"

Now, above all the shouting and singing and shuffling of many feet, a new sound was heard. It was the happy cry of a blind man whose eyes had just been opened by Jesus. Soon there was another shout of praise, and another and another as the deaf and dumb and lame gave thanks to the Great Healer. Cripples threw away their crutches and leaped for joy as the power of God made them suddenly strong again.

What a day that was! Never had the Temple seen anything like it. Never would it again.

You would think that the priests and rulers would have been glad to see so many people happy. But they were not. The Bible says that "when the chief priests and scribes saw the wonderful things that He did, and the children crying in the

46

temple, and saying, Hosanna to the Son of David; they were sore displeased."

Forcing their way through the crowd to where Jesus was standing, they asked, "Do you hear what these children are saying?"

Of course He had heard them, and He loved them for it.

"Have you never read," He asked the priests, " 'Out of the mouth of babes and sucklings Thou hast brought perfect praise' ?"

He was quoting from the eighth psalm, which the priests knew very well. It must have made them angrier than ever to have Jesus apply the text to such a moment as this.

But Jesus was right. These boys and girls were actually fulfilling prophecy. Out of their sweet, loving, innocent hearts they were giving "perfect praise" to "the Son of David," who was indeed the Son of God. Their happy songs and smiling faces were one of the dearest memories He carried with Him to the cross.

STORY 9

Vision Jesus Saw

IT WAS about this time that Philip and Andrew came up to Jesus and whispered to Him, "There are some people in the outer court who want to see You; they've come all the way from Greece."

"*I* met them first," said Philip; "they said to me, 'We would see Jesus,' so I told Andrew and we've come to tell You. Could You spare time to meet them?"

Could He! This was the most wonderful thing that could have happened just now, so near the end of His ministry.

Leaving the inner court—which was for Jews only—He went out to where the strangers were standing.

How thrilled they must have been to see the famous Teacher from Galilee! Their faces glowed with excitement as they told Him they had come from Athens, or Corinth, or maybe Thessalonica; that they had heard about His teachings and miracles and how He had even raised a man from the dead.

But if these Greeks were glad to see Jesus, He was just

48

as glad to see them, because their coming fulfilled prophecy.

For as He looked into their earnest faces He probably recalled Solomon's prayer for the strangers who would some-day come to the Temple from "a far country," having heard of God's "great name" and His "strong hand" and His "stretched out arm."

Now as He thought of all the suffering that lay ahead of Him, His face clouded with pain. "Now is My soul troubled," He said. "And what shall I say, 'Father, save Me from this hour'? No, for this purpose I have come to this hour."

Looking toward heaven He cried, "Father, glorify Thy name."

As He said this, there came a strange and wonderful sound.

Most of the people standing by thought it was thunder, but some said, "An angel has spoken to Him." Actually it was the voice of God saying, "I have glorified it, and I will glorify it again."

"This voice has come for your sake, not for Mine," said Jesus.

It had come that they might know for certain that He was indeed the Son of God.

This was the third time God had openly recognized Jesus. The first occasion was when He was baptized; the second when

He was transfigured; and the third was before these Gentiles.

"This is My beloved Son, in whom I am well pleased," He had said by the Jordan. "This is My beloved Son, in whom I am well pleased; hear ye Him," He had said on the mountaintop. Now here in the Temple He promised His Son victory no matter what might happen to Him.

Jesus was greatly cheered; and in that moment He caught a vision of the final triumph of His cause.

"Now is the judgment of this world," He cried. "Now shall the prince of this world be cast out. And I, if I be lifted up from the earth, will draw all men unto Me."

He was thinking of His death and the glorious afterward. He might be "lifted up" upon a cross, but that cross would become a mighty magnet drawing more people than had come to Him through all the years of His ministry.

They would come from far and near, from all nations and races. They would come from the west, like these Greeks, and from the east, like the Magi who had followed His star

PAINTING BY
WILLIAM HEASLIP

to Bethlehem. They would come from the north and the south and everywhere.

In their hearts would be a great hunger for truth, and light, and love, and God. One and all, they would cry with eager longing, "We would see Jesus!"

Yes! And this cry would spread ever farther and farther, growing louder and louder as it rose from thousands of men and women, boys and girls, all around the world.

"We would see Jesus! We would see Jesus!" would be the yearning of these peoples yet unborn. And they *would* see Him —the King of lovers—hanging on a cross, with hands out-stretched in love to welcome all. Falling at His feet to worship Him, they would give Him their hearts forever.

It was this glorious vision that cheered the heart of Jesus for the dark days ahead. This was "the joy that was set before Him" for which He "endured the cross, despising the shame."

PART II

Stories of the King of Sorrows

(Matthew 26:20-75; Mark 14:12-15:20; Luke 22:3-46; John
11:27-57; 13:1-18:37)

STORY 1

Feet Jesus Washed

IT IS a most interesting fact that about the same time that the Greeks arrived at the Temple, longing to see Jesus, one of His closest disciples came there to betray Him.

This disciple asked to see the chief priests, and they, curious to find out what he might have to say about his Master, invited him to talk with them.

He said that his name was Judas Iscariot and that he was one of the twelve special friends of Jesus. He had been disappointed in the Galilean Teacher, however, chiefly because all His talk about a wonderful kingdom hadn't come true. And now, well, what would they be willing to pay to find out where He stayed at night?

The priests must have been amazed that one who had followed Jesus so long should have turned against Him like this. But why should they worry? This was a break for them.

They would like to arrest Jesus at night, when nobody was about. Could Judas lead them to His secret hiding place?

55

When Satan filled the heart of Judas, one of Jesus' trusted disciples, he went to the priests and bargained with them to betray his Master into their hands for thirty pieces of silver.

He could. But how much would they pay for the information?

"How about thirty pieces of silver?" one of them asked.

Judas agreed, and the money was counted out to him. He put it in his purse and walked away, having sold his Lord and Master for the price of a slave.

Meanwhile, Jesus was planning His last meal with His disciples. To Peter and John He said, "Go and prepare the passover for us, that we may eat it."

They were to find a room big enough for thirteen people, and they asked Jesus whether He had any special place in mind.

He had; and He told them how to find it.

"When you have entered the city," He said, "a man carrying a jar of water will meet you; follow him into the house which he enters, and tell the householder, 'The Teacher says to you, Where is the guest room, where I am to eat the passover with My disciples?' And he will show you a large upper room furnished; there make ready."

They went to Jerusalem and everything turned out just as Jesus had said. They met the man carrying a jar of water and followed him to the house. Then they asked the householder whether he had a room where Jesus and His disciples could eat the Passover.

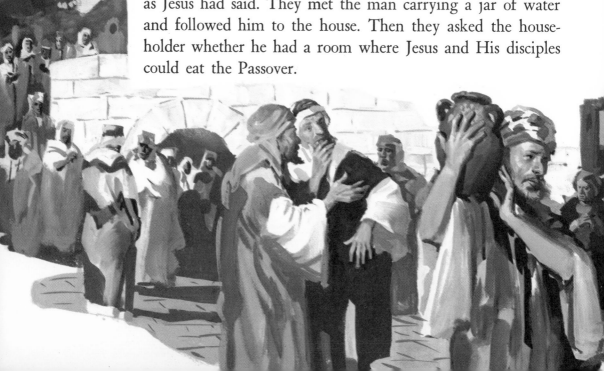

Yes, he said, he had; it was upstairs, and they were welcome to use it for the evening.

Peter and John went up and saw the room and found it to be just what they wanted. So they laid the table and put the couches in place for Jesus and the twelve to recline on— as was the custom in those days. Next they brought in basins and towels so all could wash before the meal. Then they went to a store and bought unleavened bread and unfermented wine as the Passover rules required. Next they had to buy a paschal lamb, have it inspected by the proper officials in the Temple, and kill it there. Then they cooked it.

It is quite possible that Judas, being the treasurer of the group, actually paid for this lamb that was the symbol of Christ, the "Lamb of God," and that either Peter or John took its life.

At the time agreed on, all the disciples arrived at the upper room—Peter, Andrew, James, John, Philip, Bartholomew, Thomas, Matthew, James the son of Alphaeus, Thaddaeus, Simon, and Judas Iscariot.

Judas, remembering what he had told the priests, must have felt very uncomfortable, not knowing whether the others suspected his treason. Yet he made a show of loyalty by taking the couch next to Jesus. John took the couch on the other side of the Master, so that it appeared that his head was lying on Jesus' breast.

As they all took their places Jesus seemed more solemn than usual, as if something was troubling Him. It was hard to believe that, but a little while before, He had been the center of the great scene in the Temple, healing the sick, overturning the tables of the money-changers, and hearing the children call Him the Son of David.

Something *was* troubling Him. And it was not that He knew only a few hours remained before He would be arrested and crucified. He was worried about these friends of His and how little they seemed to understand of all He had tried to teach them. They were still expecting Him to set up an earthly kingdom, and still scheming who should be the greatest in it. Each one wanted to be prime minister, or treasurer, and it wasn't going to be like that at all.

To Jesus it seemed very, very sad that they should be thinking thoughts like these when their little world was about to fall

apart. What else could He do than He had already done to make them see that they must be humble and unselfish or they would never see His kingdom at all?

There was one more thing He could do, and He decided to try it.

Rising from His couch, He took a towel, poured water into a basin, and began to wash the disciples' feet, probably beginning with Judas, who sat next to Him.

One of the group should have attended to this before the meal began, but no one was willing to do it. There was too much pride in their hearts. Now, amazed, they saw their Master, their Lord, their King, doing this humblest of duties.

PAINTING BY PAUL REMMEY

Peter couldn't stand it. When Jesus came to him he cried, "You shall never wash my feet!"

"If I do not wash you," said Jesus, "you have no part with Me."

At this Peter answered, "Lord, not my feet only, but also my hands and my head!"

This was not necessary, Jesus said, though I feel sure He loved Peter for saying it. Then He continued His work till He had washed the feet of all.

After He had returned to His couch He spoke very plainly. "Do you know what I have done to you?" He asked. "You call Me Teacher and Lord; and you are right, for so I am. If I then, your Lord and Teacher, have washed your feet, you also ought to wash one another's feet. For I have given you an example, that you also should do as I have done to you."

Then looking earnestly from one to another, He said very solemnly, "Truly, truly, I say to you, a servant is not greater than his master; nor is he who is sent greater than he who sent him. If you know these things, blessed are you if you do them."

That was the hardest lesson Jesus ever taught. The hardest to remember, I mean. The hardest to follow. Maybe you and I need to learn it today.

Are you willing to wash anybody's feet? Even the feet of the Judas in your life?

60

STORY 2

Farewell Party

THAT meal in the upper room is called the Last Supper, and so it was. These thirteen people never ate together again.

In a sense it was a farewell party. Jesus knew it was, if the others didn't. He saw that in a very little while they would all be scattered like sheep being chased by wolves. This was their last peaceful time together, and He wanted them to remember it always.

"Having loved His own who were in the world, He loved them unto the end," and here, at this final meeting with His followers, the tender compassion of the King of lovers was seen in all its beauty and gentleness.

The Bible says that "as they were eating, Jesus took bread, and blessed, and broke it, and gave it to the disciples and said, 'Take, eat; this is My body.' And He took a cup, and when He had given thanks He gave it to them, saying, 'Drink of it, all of you; for this is My blood of the covenant, which is poured

out for many for the forgiveness of sins. I tell you I shall not drink again of this fruit of the vine until that day when I drink it new with you in My Father's kingdom.' "

Never before had He spoken so clearly about His death, or how it would bring "forgiveness of sins" to many. Years afterward, as the disciples thought about what happened that night, they saw that the breaking of the bread was a symbol of the breaking of His body on the cross, and that the cup of wine He gave them to drink was a symbol of the blood He shed on Calvary. That is why His followers have shared bread and wine together ever since. These simple things have become two sacred symbols of the Christian faith.

When the apostle Paul tried to tell the church at Corinth what happened at that farewell party he said, "The Lord Jesus

62

on the night when He was betrayed took bread, and when He had given thanks, He broke it, and said, . . . 'Do this in remembrance of Me.' In the same way also the cup, after supper, saying, 'This cup is the new covenant in My blood. Do this, as often as you drink it, in remembrance of Me.' For as often as you eat this bread and drink the cup, you proclaim the Lord's death until He comes."

Notice how Jesus spoke of both the bread and the wine as being "in remembrance" of Him. He wanted them to remember Him—always. Today the same symbols are to help us to remember Him "until He comes."

One of the sweetest things Jesus did that night was to offer the bread and wine to Judas. Full well He knew what Judas had done, yet He said to him, as to all the others, "Re-

63

member Me." It was enough to soften the hardest heart, but Judas had gone too far.

By and by Jesus startled everyone at the table by saying, "One of you will betray Me."

They couldn't believe it. They thought He must be mistaken. Each one wondered whether at any time he had said or done anything that might get the Master into trouble.

One by one they asked Him, "Lord, is it I?"

He wouldn't answer, so Peter beckoned to John, who was next to Jesus, to find out who was the traitor.

John whispered to Jesus, "Lord, who is it?"

Softly Jesus replied, "It is he to whom I shall give this morsel when I have dipped it."

When Jesus had dipped the morsel He gave it to Judas.

At this moment Judas, who had kept silent till now, joined the others in asking, "Master, is it I?"

No doubt he thought he would take suspicion off himself by doing so. But Jesus answered him, "You have said so," which was another way of saying, "Yes."

Then Jesus whispered to Judas, so the others could not hear, "What you are going to do, do quickly."

At this Judas rose and went out. "And it was night."

The others thought that Jesus had asked him to go and buy something for the feast or to give something to the poor, so carefully did the Master try to cover up the sin of this wretched traitor. Could love go further? Surely only the King of lovers, and the King of sorrows could have loved so bad a man so long and so much.

STORY 3

Last Loving Words

JESUS did not call His disciples to that upper room just to eat the Passover. He had something else in mind as well. He knew that this would be His last chance to talk with them all together, and there was so much He wanted to say before He left them.

After the meal was over, and Judas had gone out into the night, the rest gathered closer about their beloved Master. In the dim light of the little oil lamps on the table they listened with growing sadness as He spoke His last loving words of counsel and cheer.

"Little children," He said to them, "yet a little while I am with you. You will seek Me, and as I said to the Jews so now I say to you, 'Where I am going you cannot come.' "

Fancy calling these grown men "little children"! Yet that is what they were to Him. He loved them as if they were His own dear boys. And it made Him sad to think that, like lost children looking for their mother or father, they would search for Him after His crucifixion and not find Him.

Then He gave them some good advice—the best advice any father could give to his children. "A new commandment I give to you," He said, "that you love one another; even as I have loved you, that you also love one another. By this all men will know that you are My disciples, if you have love for one another."

Of all the beautiful things Jesus said, this is perhaps the loveliest. "Love one another!" Be kind to one another. Be forgiving to one another. Be tenderhearted to one another. Be thoughtful of one another's needs. Forget one another's faults.

This would be the badge of His followers. They wouldn't need to wear a gold pin or some special kind of cap, or gown, or collar. Through all the years to come, anywhere, any time, Christians would be known by their love—love shown in tender words and kindly deeds.

"By *this* shall all men know you belong to Me." How much "this" means! If we don't love our brothers, our sisters, our friends, our neighbors, then we don't belong to Him. If we don't treat them as Jesus would treat them, we are not His disciples. We are not Christians. We can have no part in His kingdom. That's something to think about, isn't it?

At this point Peter broke in to say that he loved Jesus so much that he would follow Him always, anywhere. "I will lay down my life for you!" he said.

"Will you?" said Jesus. "Before the cock crows twice you will deny Me thrice."

Peter was silenced. He couldn't understand what Jesus meant. Why, he would never deny his Master. Never! Certainly not that very night!

Meanwhile, Jesus went on to talk about His return and how some day He would come back and gather all His dear followers to Himself and take them to the "many mansions" in His Father's house. There would be a lovely home for every one of them in His glorious kingdom.

But soon He was back on the subject of love. There would be no mansion for anybody who did not have love in his heart. And love is shown by keeping His commandments.

"If you love Me," He said, "keep My commandments."

Again, "If a man loves Me, he will keep My word, and My Father will love him, and we will come to him and make our home with him."

What a sweet thing for Jesus to say! The great God of heaven will make His home with any man or woman, boy or girl, in whose heart true, unselfish love is to be found. It may be hard to understand, but it is true. And it just shows how God prizes love—pure, beautiful love—above everything else in the world.

If you want your heart to be God's home, if you want Him to live with you and keep you all your days, this is the way. All you have to do is to love other people as much, or more, than you love yourself. And when God sees this love in your heart He will come, by His Holy Spirit, and dwell with you and be your Comforter, Guide, and Friend the rest of your life.

"The Counselor, the Holy Spirit, whom the Father will send in My name, He will teach you all things, and bring to your remembrance all that I have said to you."

Now the meeting was drawing to a close. Looking around upon His faithful friends, who meant so much to Him and whom He loved so dearly, Jesus said, very tenderly, "Peace I leave with you; My peace I give to you; not as the world gives do I give to you. Let not your hearts be troubled, neither let them be afraid."

Right to the last He tried to cheer them up. But it was difficult. Though He was the one who was about to suffer, they were the ones who were afraid. They hated to think He was going to leave them. And when He suggested that they sing a hymn I'm afraid some of them were too choked up to do much about it. It was the voice of Jesus that could be heard

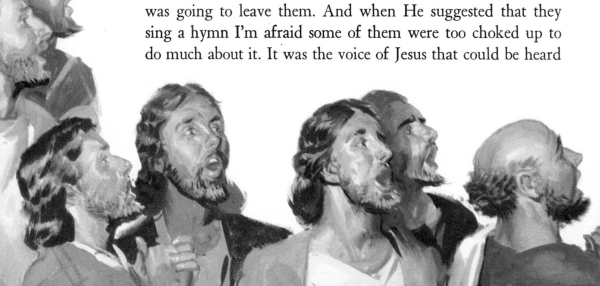

above all, courageously singing the beautiful Passover song:

"O praise the Lord, all ye nations:
Praise Him all ye people.
For His merciful kindness is great toward us:
And the truth of the Lord endureth for ever.
Praise ye the Lord."

Then there was silence, broken no doubt by the half-suppressed sobs of those who couldn't keep from crying.

"Rise, let us go hence," said Jesus, and they went—out into the quiet, moonlit streets of Jerusalem, out past the sleepy guards at the city gate, out toward the Mount of Olives and Gethsemane.

The farewell party was over. Yet not the memories. Could they ever forget how Jesus had sung that last sweet song? Could they ever forget all His final words of counsel and how He had tried to cheer them up with one precious promise after another? Could they ever forget how He had washed their feet? Could they ever forget how He had given them bread to eat and wine to drink in remembrance of Him? No indeed. Not in a thousand, thousand years.
Not through all eternity.

STORY 4

"Please Look After Them"

JUST where it happened nobody knows. It could have been in the upper room. It could have been at some stopping place on the winding road down from Jerusalem. Or it could have been in Gethsemane. But somewhere that night Jesus prayed His last beautiful prayer for His disciples.

All of them must have heard it, but only John remembered it well enough to write it down so that we might know what He said and how much He loved them all. You will find this prayer in the seventeenth chapter of his Gospel.

Lifting up His eyes toward heaven He said, "Father, the hour is come; glorify Thy Son, that Thy Son also may glorify Thee: as Thou hast given Him power over all flesh, that He should give eternal life to as many as Thou hast given Him.

"And this is life eternal, that they might know Thee the only true God, and Jesus Christ, whom Thou hast sent.

"I have glorified Thee on the earth; I have finished the work which Thou gavest Me to do.

70

"And now, O Father, glorify Thou Me with Thine own self with the glory which I had with Thee before the world was.

"I have manifested Thy name unto the men which Thou gavest Me out of the world: Thine they were, and Thou gavest them Me; and they have kept Thy word."

He didn't mention their mistakes; or any of the foolish things they had said; or how jealous they had been of one another. When talking with His Father He just told the good things about them and asked Him to watch over them always.

"I pray for them: I pray not for the world, but for them which Thou hast given Me; for they are Thine. And all Mine are Thine, and Thine are Mine; and I am glorified in them.

"And now I am no more in the world, but these are in the world, and I come to Thee. Holy Father, keep through Thine own name those whom Thou hast given Me, that they may be one, as We are. . . .

"I pray not that Thou shouldest take them out of the world, but that Thou shouldest keep them from the evil.

"They are not of the world, even as I am not of the world.

"Sanctify them through Thy truth: Thy word is truth."

Then He thought of others who, in years to come, would believe on Him through the witness of His faithful little band of disciples.

"Neither pray I for these alone," He said, "but for them also which shall believe on Me through their word; that they all may be one; as Thou, Father, art in Me, and I in Thee,

that they also may be one in us. . . . I in them, and Thou in Me, that they may be made perfect in one; and that the world may know that Thou hast sent Me, and hast loved them, as Thou hast loved Me."

"Father," He pleaded, and you can almost feel the earnestness in His voice as He spoke, "Father, I will that they also whom Thou hast given Me, be with Me where I am; that they may behold My glory, which Thou hast given Me: for Thou lovedst Me before the foundation of the world.

"O righteous Father, the world hath not known Thee: but I have known Thee, and these have known that Thou hast sent Me. And I have declared unto them Thy name, and will declare it: that the love wherewith Thou hast loved Me may be in them, and I in them."

So His prayer ended. And what a beautiful prayer it was! So simple, so trusting, so thoughtful of others! It was, in fact, just a lovely farewell prayer for His dearest earthly friends. "Please look after them when I'm gone" was the yearning of His heart. "Please keep them from evil. Help them to love one another. And may we all meet again in the glory land some day."

And isn't it wonderful to think that this sweet prayer was not only for those eleven lonesome disciples but for everybody else who would love Him, all down the years. He was praying for you and me, too, that we might be kept from all evil, that our hearts might be filled with love, and that we might share heaven with Him at last.

STORY 5

Night in a Garden

≈≈≈≈≈≈≈≈≈≈≈≈≈≈≈≈≈≈≈≈≈≈≈≈≈≈≈≈

I T WAS now very late, long past the disciples' usual bedtime. All of them were tired out and very, very sleepy.
Some were already stretched out on the ground, sound
asleep.

An eerie silence filled the Garden of Gethsemane, broken
only by the sighing of the wind in the olive trees, the distant
barking of a dog, or the shout of a sentinel upon the city walls.

To those who were still awake Jesus said, "Sit here, while
I go yonder and pray."

Then He took Peter, James, and John and walked some
yards away from the others.

"My soul is very sorrowful, even to death," He said to
them. "Stay here, and watch with Me."

He was lonely, and wanted their company.

Going forward a few paces, "He fell on His face and
prayed."

"My Father," He cried, "if it be possible, let this cup pass

from Me; nevertheless, not as I will, but as Thou wilt."

He knew what was going to happen on the morrow—all the shame and the pain and the cruelty of crucifixion—and here alone, in the pale moonlight, the thought of it seemed too terrible to bear. Worse still was the thought that He, who had never sinned, who hated sin, was to be judged a sinner and punished as one.

How cruel is injustice and how hard to take!

Have you ever been blamed for something you never did or even thought of doing? If so, you know a little of how Jesus must have felt that night. Becoming man's sin bearer meant that He was going to be blamed for everybody's sins —all the wrong that had been done since Eve first sinned in another garden, long ago—and it didn't seem fair. It wasn't fair. But there was just no other way for Him to deliver man from sin's penalty and power.

As the prophet Isaiah wrote—and Jesus knew the words by heart—"the Lord hath laid on Him the iniquity of us all." He became "sin for us, who knew no sin," said the apostle Paul long after. That's why being our Saviour hurt so much.

Just as you or I might have done, He prayed, "Please, God, don't let it happen." Yet He knew it must happen. For this He had come from heaven. Willingly He had offered Himself as the Lamb of God to take away the sins of the world. And now the Lamb must be sacrificed. There was nothing else to do. If He were to give up now, there would be no hope, no salvation, no heaven, for anybody. He knew that. And that's why He said, "Not My will, but Thine, be done."

75

While His tired disciples slept, Jesus struggled in Gethsemane with the burden of the sins of the world which were about to be rolled on Him at Calvary as the Redeemer of men.

His love was being tested to the limit. He could so easily have run away and hidden from His enemies. He could have just disappeared as He did when the people of Nazareth tried to push Him over a cliff. But He didn't. He stayed true to His purpose. He loved us all too much to do anything else.

Then there were the prophecies Jesus had studied from His youth up. God had foretold the coming of a Saviour, the town where He would be born, and the time He would be put to death. That time was about to be fulfilled, and as the Son of God He knew that He could not draw back from the sufferings that were before Him.

Returning to the three disciples, He found that they, like all the others, had fallen asleep. Peter stirred a little, so Jesus said to him, "What, could you not watch with Me one hour? Watch and pray, that you enter not into temptation: the spirit indeed is willing, but the flesh is weak."

Then "He went away again the second time, and prayed, saying, O My Father, if this cup may not pass away from Me, except I drink it, Thy will be done."

By and by he returned to the three disciples again. Now they were fast asleep. So "He left them, and went away again, and prayed the third time, saying the same words."

"And being in an agony He prayed more earnestly: and His sweat was as it were great drops of blood falling down to the ground."

It was not just the dread of dying that crushed Him so, but the thought that He must carry the whole fearful burden of human sin. That awful night—

76

"All the sins of man since time began
    Were laid, dear Lord, on Thee."

It was almost more than He could bear. But now something wonderful happened. "There appeared an angel unto Him from heaven, strengthening Him."

The Bible doesn't say which angel, but it could have been Gabriel who, thirty-three years before, had foretold Jesus' birth to Mary.

I wish I knew what the angel said to Jesus that "strengthened" Him so. Perhaps he took the Master's poor bloodstained head in his lap and said, "Courage, O Son of God! All creation is watching You! All heaven is counting on You! You must not fail. Not now. Victory is sure. These trials will soon be over. In a little while You will be home again. And how happy we shall be to welcome You and crown You Lord of all!"

Rising from His knees at last, Jesus went back once more to where Peter, James, and John were still lying on the ground, deep in slumber.

"Sleep on now, and take your rest," He said to them. "Behold, the hour is at hand, and the Son of man is betrayed into the hands of sinners."

STORY 6

Betrayed by a Traitor

H OW LONG Jesus stayed alone we do not know. But in a little while, hearing noises in the distance, He guessed that His enemies were on their way to arrest Him.

"Rise, let us be going," He said to the sleeping disciples. Rubbing their eyes, they sat up, scarcely half awake.

"Why, what's the matter?" they muttered.

"See," He said to them, pointing to the lanterns and torches that were moving slowly up the hillside. "My betrayer is at hand."

It was a rowdy mob that came, armed with swords and clubs, sent by "the chief priests and elders of the people."

The disciples looked on in surprise and fear. They had heard Jesus tell about trouble to come, but they hadn't expected this. Surely He wouldn't let Himself be taken by such horrid people!

Peter reached for the sword he had brought with him.

BETRAYED BY A TRAITOR

At least *he* would make a fight for it. Let one of them so much as put a hand on the Master and he'd learn a lesson he wouldn't soon forget. Oh, why hadn't the rest brought swords, too? Then they would have stood a chance against this crowd!

Now they caught sight of Judas. Judas! Right in front of the mob, as though one of its leaders. What was he doing there? Surely he had not joined their enemies! Had he not eaten with them in the upper room only a few short hours ago!

Now Jesus walked boldly toward the mob.

"Whom do you seek?" He asked.

"Jesus of Nazareth," they cried, not recognizing Him in the darkness.

"I am He," said Jesus.

At this the whole crowd fell to the ground in terror. Perhaps it was the glorious light shining from His face that frightened them, or the presence of the angel who had strengthened Him.

Presently Judas staggered to his feet and came to where Jesus was standing.

"Hail, Master," he said, and kissed Him. This was the sign he had agreed on with the priests. "The one I shall kiss is the man," he had told them; "seize Him."

"Friend, why are you here?" asked Jesus. "Would you betray the Son of man with a kiss?"

Now the ruffians were surging forward again, angry that they had let themselves be scared by this one unarmed man. Hands reached out to grab Him.

Peter came running up. "Shall we strike with the sword?" he cried. And before Jesus could stop him, the big fisherman had brought his weapon down on the head of Malchus, one of the high priest's servants, lopping off his right ear.

The man yelled in agony and put up his hand to stop the flow of blood. But another hand got there first. Crying, "No more of this!" Jesus touched the wound, healing it at once. When the man felt the place to see what had happened, he found his ear restored as it had been before.

BETRAYED BY A TRAITOR

The miracle gave Jesus a few moments more of freedom.

Turning to Peter He said, "Put your sword back into its place; for all who take the sword will perish by the sword. Do you think that I cannot appeal to My Father, and He will at once send Me more than twelve legions of angels? But how then should the scriptures be fulfilled, that it must be so?"

Of course He could have called the angels to save Him, and how glad they would have been to come! Tens of thousands would have come sweeping down the skies at a single word. But He wouldn't speak that word. It would have upset the whole plan of salvation and made all the great prophecies of the Messiah meaningless.

Now He turned on the mob and rebuked them for coming out to arrest Him with swords and clubs as if He were a common thief.

"Day after day I sat in the temple teaching," He said, "and you did not seize Me. But all this has taken place, that the scriptures of the prophets might be fulfilled."

How important those old Scriptures were to Him! But the crowd wasn't listening. Already the soldiers were binding His hands so that they might lead Him as a prisoner to the high priest.

Thinking more of His disciples than of Himself, Jesus said, "If I am the one you want, let these men go."

But He need not have said it. They had gone already.

Taking advantage of the darkness, they had scattered in all directions. They all "forsook Him and fled."

STORY 7

Denied by a Friend

JUST where all the disciples went that night we do not know. Some may have gone to nearby Bethany to break the awful news to Lazarus, Mary, and Martha. Others may have taken cover on the wooded hillside till danger was past. So far as we know only Peter and John kept up with the mob as it hurried Jesus back to the city.

John, who had friends in the high priest's palace, managed to get inside and watch the trial of his beloved Master.

Peter followed "afar off," but when he arrived, John got him into the servants' quarters, where he ran into a lot of trouble.

The story John tells us is a very sad one. Jesus was taken first to Annas, then to Caiaphas, who presided over the Sanhedrin, the governing body of Israel at that time. Evidently some of its members were waiting for Jesus when He was brought in. Others hurried to the palace as soon as they knew He had been captured.

DENIED BY A FRIEND

It was illegal to hold a trial in the middle of the night, but so great was the hatred of the chief priests for Jesus that they were ready to break their own laws to get rid of Him.

Most likely the chief reason for the night trial was that they wanted to have it all over before the people who loved Jesus found out what had been done. If He were already condemned to death, what could anybody do about it?

If only there had been a few children about, I am sure they would have done what they could to help. One of them at least would have called out, "Leave Him alone! He's our friend!" But, alas, they were all in bed!

So there stood Jesus, alone and friendless, in the midst of the priests and rabbis. How they hated Him! They were jealous because He was so popular with the common people; they were envious of His power to heal the sick; they were angry because the truth and beauty of His teachings showed up the foolishness of theirs. Now they had Him where they wanted Him, and they would never let Him go.

There was no chance for fair play at such a trial. Jesus was as good as condemned before He got there.

The high priest began by asking Jesus about His disciples and His teachings, suggesting that He was trying to form a secret society. Jesus said there was nothing secret about His work. "I have spoken openly to the world," He said; "I have always taught in synagogues and in the Temple, where all Jews come together; I have said nothing secretly. Why do you ask Me? Ask those who have heard Me, what I said to them; they know what I said."

At this one of the officers standing by struck Jesus with his hand, saying, "Is that how you answer the high priest?"

With wonderful patience Jesus kept calm and respectful.

"If I have spoken wrongly, bear witness to the wrong," He said; "but if I have spoken rightly, why do you strike Me?"

Now false witnesses were called in to say that Jesus had said and done things that were wrong. But they didn't agree. One contradicted another. The trial was getting nowhere. Then two men came forward and declared, "This fellow said, 'I am able to destroy the temple of God, and to build it in three days.'"

"What have you to say to this?" asked the high priest.

Jesus did not reply. He *had* said something like this, but not about the Temple these men were thinking about. He had meant the temple of His body that He would raise up in three days after His death—but what was the use of telling these people? They wouldn't understand.

"Have you no answer to make?" roared the high priest. "What is it that these men testify against you?"

DENIED BY A FRIEND

Still Jesus kept silent, and all the cruel mob wondered.

Having no more witnesses, the high priest decided he must try to get Jesus to condemn Himself. Rising to his feet, he cried, "I adjure you by the living God, tell us if you are the Christ, the Son of God."

Jesus had to answer now, for He couldn't deny His divinity or His mission, though it meant His death.

"You have said so," He said calmly, which was the same as saying, "Yes." Then He added, "I tell you, hereafter you will see the Son of man seated on the right hand of power, and coming on the clouds of heaven."

At this the high priest tore his robes in fury. "He has uttered blasphemy!" he shrieked. "Why do we still need witnesses? You have now heard His blasphemy. What is your judgment?"

"He deserves death!" they cried together.

They would have killed Him right then had they dared. But they couldn't put anyone to death without permission of the Roman governor. So they sent Him, bound, to Pilate.

DENIED BY A FRIEND

While Jesus waited, men spat on Him and struck Him. Someone covered His head with a sack while the mob sneered, "Prophesy to us, you Christ! Who is it who struck you?"

Meanwhile in the servants' hall Peter had been having a hard time too. As he warmed his hands by the fire one of the maids said to him, "Weren't you also with Jesus of Galilee?"

"No!" said Peter. "Never saw the man."

As the maid went away a cock crowed, but Peter was too worried to notice it.

A little later another servant came over to him and, after taking a good look, said to the others who were standing around, "This fellow *was* with Jesus of Nazareth. He's the one who cut off Malchus' ear!"

"I don't know what you're talking about!" cried Peter with an oath.

But the others were not satisfied. They said, "You *are* a Galilean! Your accent betrays you. You *are* one of them."

At this Peter began to curse and to swear, saying, "I am not. I don't know anything about Him."

Just then the cock crowed again, and Peter remembered how Jesus had said to him, "Before the cock crows twice, you will deny Me thrice."

Suddenly, looking up, he caught sight of Jesus, His hands bound, and marks of suffering on His face.

"And the Lord turned, and looked upon Peter."

Their eyes met.

Peter was all broken up. Leaping to his feet in shame and sorrow, he rushed outside "and wept bitterly."

87

← PAINTING BY MANNING DE V. LEE ⓒ 1957, BY REVIEW AND HERALD

After Peter for the third time in the court of the high priest had denied knowing his Master, Jesus looked at him as a soldier ed Him away, and it broke Peter's heart.

STORY 8

Condemned by Enemies

EARING that Jesus had been condemned to death, Judas suddenly felt sorry for what he had done. He wished he had never taken those thirty pieces of silver. He would return them. Perhaps if the priests got their money back, they would set Jesus free. But it was too late. They didn't want the money.

Rushing in before them, he cried, "I have sinned in betraying innocent blood!"

"What is that to us?" they sneered. "See to it yourself."

Judas meant nothing to them now. He had done the job they had wanted him to do, and now they were ready to push him out of their way.

"Here's your money!" cried Judas, throwing the coins at them.

Then, as the silver pieces scattered over the marble floor he ran from the palace, out along the darkened, deserted streets, to the city gate—perhaps the very gate through which Jesus was to pass later that very day. Somewhere beyond it, alone, ashamed and terrified, he found a tree and hanged himself.

It's worth remembering that both Judas and Jesus died the same day. Both died on trees. One died by his own hand, the other by the hands of His enemies. One died a traitor, the other a hero. One helped nobody by his death. The other saved a world.

Back at the palace the priests looked at the thirty pieces of silver on the floor and decided to pick them up. But they were puzzled what to do with them. "This is blood money," they said; "we can't put it back in the treasury." So they called a committee meeting and decided to use it to buy the potter's field, "to bury strangers in." It was still called the Field of Blood when, years later, Matthew wrote his Gospel.

Meanwhile Jesus was being pushed and dragged in the midst of a jeering mob to the home of the Roman governor. It was still early in the morning when they arrived there, and I am sure Pilate was not at all pleased at being disturbed at

such an hour. He must have wondered, too, why the priests couldn't wait for their prisoner to be judged at a proper time.

As for Jesus, He must have been very, very tired. He hadn't slept since Wednesday night, and it was now Friday morning. Hour after hour He had stood before His tormentors, being slapped, beaten, and spat upon. Since His arrest in Gethsemane He had had no food, no rest, not even one comforting word from a single friendly soul.

Yet He had uttered no word of complaint or talked back in anger to those who had treated Him so shamefully. He was "like a lamb that is led to the slaughter, and like a sheep that before its shearers is dumb, so He opened not His mouth."

Often during that terrible night He must have thought how ungrateful these people were. He had tried so hard to be friends with them and help them. Some of them He had healed of various diseases. And this was how they repaid Him!

Because it was Passover time the Jews would not go into

90

Pilate's judgment hall. They thought they would defile themselves—as though they hadn't done that already by laying hands on the sacred person of the Son of God! So they stayed outside, and Jesus went in alone with his Roman guard.

Pilate looked at the prisoner and was much surprised. He had expected to see a violent criminal, not a quiet, dignified gentleman like this. There must be some mistake, he thought, and went out to speak with the chief priests.

"What charge do you bring against this man?" he asked.

"If He wasn't an evildoer, we wouldn't have brought Him to you," they answered rudely.

"Well," said Pilate, "take Him yourselves and judge Him by your own law."

"It is not lawful for us to put any man to death," they said.

To death! Why did they want to put such a man as this to death?

Someone shouted, "We found this fellow perverting the nation, and forbidding to give tribute to Caesar." Another cried, "He says that He is Christ, a king."

Soon many were shouting all sorts of accusations.

Pilate went back and spoke to Jesus.

"Do you hear how many things they testify against you?" he asked. Jesus said nothing. He "gave him no answer, not even to a single charge; so that the governor wondered greatly."

Pilate had never seen anyone behave like this. Most prisoners denied all charges with anger. But this one refused to defend Himself. Was He guilty or innocent?

"Are you the King of the Jews?" he asked.

91

At this Jesus asked a question of the governor: "Do you say this of your own accord or did others say it to you about me?"

Jesus wanted to find out whether Pilate was really interested in Him as the true King of the Jews. It was the governor's chance to accept Jesus and be saved. He passed it by.

"Am I a Jew?" Pilate asked. "Your own nation and the chief priests have handed you over to me; what have you done?"

Jesus answered in those wonderful, never-to-be-forgotten words: "My kingdom is not of this world: if My kingdom were of this world, then would My servants fight, that I should not be delivered to the Jews: but now is My kingdom not from hence."

"So you are a king?" asked Pilate.

Jesus said He was, adding, "To this end was I born, and for this cause came I into the world, that I should bear witness unto the truth."

Pilate was puzzled. What sort of king was this who wanted nothing but truth?

"What is truth?" he asked. But he did not wait for an answer. The shouts of the mob were growing louder and louder. He went outside and called for silence. Then he said, "I find in Him no fault at all."

At this the crowd seemed to go mad with rage.

92

CONDEMNED BY ENEMIES

Someone yelled, "He stirs up the people, teaching throughout all Judea, from Galilee even to this place."

This gave Pilate an idea. He remembered that Herod, the ruler of Galilee, was in town. Why not let him decide this case?

So he sent Jesus, in the care of a Roman guard, to the house where Herod was staying. The mob followed, shouting insults.

Herod was glad to see Jesus, having heard many stories about Him. Once he had been worried that Jesus might be John the Baptist, risen from the dead; but he had long since ceased to worry about that. He hoped that the famous healer would perform a miracle for him. But Jesus would not do so. He was no common magician; nor was He there merely to amuse the man who had murdered His cousin.

Meanwhile "the chief priests and scribes stood by, vehemently accusing Him."

Still Jesus kept silent. No matter how false and wicked the charges made against Him, He would not let Himself get angry.

Herod did not know what to do with the strange

prisoner who just stood there calmly looking at him with sad, accusing eyes. Suddenly he went into a rage and let his soldiers mock Jesus and strike Him. As a last cruel joke he had them put a "gorgeous robe" on Him. Then he sent Him back to Pilate.

Now there was another procession through the streets, with more jeers and sneers and shouts of hatred. Jesus must have wondered how much longer He could stand it. Then He remembered that the hour for the slaying of the Passover lamb was drawing near. It wouldn't be long now.

Pilate was not pleased when Jesus was brought back to him. Now he would have to settle this matter himself.

Going out again to the raging crowd gathered before the judgment hall, he told them how he had questioned the prisoner and found Him not guilty. So had Herod. "Therefore," he said, "because nothing worthy of death has been done by Him, I will therefore chastise Him and release Him."

"No!" they yelled. "Away with this man, and release to us Barabbas."

"What then shall I do with Jesus?" asked Pilate.

"Crucify Him!" they cried.

"Why, what evil has He done?"

"Crucify Him, crucify Him!" was their only answer.

PART III

Stories of the King of Sufferers

(MATTHEW 27:20-66; MARK 15:21-47; LUKE 23:18-56; JOHN 19:1-42)

STORY 1

Rejected for a Robber

WHO WAS this Barabbas whom the crowd asked Pilate to release?

The Bible says he was a robber and a murderer, the leader of a riot in the city. The man had a very bad record, but a most interesting name.

It wasn't an ordinary name at all, like David or Peter or John or Stephen. It was just "Son of Papa"—*Bar* meaning "son" and *abba* meaning "papa."

That was a strange name for a mother to give her little boy, yet it was big with meaning, as things turned out.

I can imagine that as a boy Barabbas was always getting into trouble of one kind or another. He may well have been the ringleader of all the naughty boys in the village where he lived.

He must have been born about the same time as John the Baptist, but whether he met the great preacher we do not know. He may have mixed with the crowds of people by the

9-7

← PAINTING BY MANNING DE V. LEE © 1957, BY REVIEW AND HERALD

Having lost all sense of justice the hateful, cruel mob shouted to Pilate to let Barabbas the murderer go free and to turn the innocent Saviour over to them that they might crucifiy Him.

Jordan and heard John say, "Bring forth therefore fruits worthy of repentance!" Somewhere in Palestine, too, he may have listened to the gentle pleading of Jesus as He said, "Come unto Me, all ye that labour and are heavy laden, and I will give you rest."

But if Barabbas ever did hear these words, he certainly did not heed them. He turned away from God and all religion. His heart became hard and cruel. With a group of worldly young men like himself he started a riot and committed murder. For this he was arrested and thrown into prison.

How grieved his mother must have been when she learned what had happened! And how worried Barabbas must have been, lying there in the dungeon, waiting for his punishment! Condemned to death by crucifixion, he could hardly sleep for terror at the thought of it.

Days passed—long, long days—and longer nights. At last he heard carpenters at work in the courtyard, shaping his cross, and he knew the dreaded moment was close at hand.

Then one morning—very early—he was roused by a great commotion outside the prison. Through the window of his cell came the sound of loud, angry voices.

Louder and louder they grew. It seemed as though thousands of people were shouting for vengeance on somebody. Who could it be? Who could have stirred up the whole city like this, and at such an hour?

And now, what was that?

"Barabbas! We want Barabbas!"

REJECTED FOR A ROBBER

His name! Yes, they were shouting his name.

O dreadful thought! They wanted to kill him, perhaps to tear him limb from limb, perhaps to have him crucified at once!

Suddenly he heard a rattling of keys. The jailer! Perhaps he had come to hand him over to the angry crowd.

The cell door creaked open. Soldiers entered and ordered him to rise and go with them. Tremblingly he obeyed.

Up the dank stairway, along stone corridors, marched the guard and their prisoner. Where could they be taking him?

Presently, entering the governor's palace, Barabbas found himself face to face with none other than Pontius Pilate himself! And there, beyond him, was that angry, seething crowd, still shouting, "Barabbas! Release to us Barabbas!"

Then his eyes rested upon Someone else—a sad and lonely figure standing near Pilate.

"Surely I have seen that man before!" he thought. "Why, that is Jesus of Nazareth! That is the famous teacher whom all the people love. What is He doing here? Surely He has committed no crime."

Then Pilate spoke to the crowd. "Whom will ye that I release unto you?" he asked, "Barabbas, or Jesus which is called Christ?"

"Barabbas!" shrieked the crowd again. "Barabbas!"

Pilate turned to the soldiers. "Let him go," he said. "Then released he Barabbas unto them."

Bounding down the steps, Barabbas could hardly contain himself for joy. This was too wonderful for words. Instead

of being tortured and crucified, as he had expected to be, he was free! Free! Pilate himself had released him!

What happened to Barabbas after that we do not know. So far as the Bible story goes, he was lost in the crowd on that dreadful day. Perhaps—who knows?—his wicked heart was touched as he realized that Jesus took his place and bore his cross.

Did you ever stop to think how wonderful it is that it was a man called Barabbas whose cross it was that Jesus carried? Being only "Son of Papa," he stands for every boy and every girl who ever lived, no matter how bad and naughty. If his name had been John or Peter or Stephen or David, some might have thought that Jesus bore the cross for one person in particular. Then there would have been just a chance that some poor, needy, sinful soul might have felt left out. So in the providence of God the one whose place Jesus took, whose cross he bore on the day of His crucifixion, was just Barabbas, "Son of Papa."

From that moment on, everyone could feel sure that he was included in the glorious salvation that Jesus provided. Today, nearly two thousand years later, every son and daughter of Adam, every boy and girl in every nation under heaven, may say with confidence, "He died for me."

~~~~~~~~~~

STORY 2

Helped by an African

~~~~~~~~~~

W HILE Pilate was seated on the judgment seat a servant drew near, bowed low, and handed him a message. Opening the note, Pilate found to his surprise that it was from his wife. It read: "Have . . . nothing to do with that just man: for I have suffered many things this day in a dream because of Him."

This woman may well have been a secret disciple of Jesus, of whom there were many in Jerusalem. At least she was sure He was a good man who did not deserve to be punished.

Just what she saw in her dream, the Bible does not say, but it could have been the story of a crucified man coming back from the grave to become King of the whole world. Whatever it was, it frightened her so much that she could not rest until she had urged her husband to let Him go.

Pilate should have heeded the warning, but he didn't. He was afraid of the anger of the Jewish priests and rulers and the report they might send to the Roman emperor about him.

101

By this time he was sure Jesus was innocent, and he should have released Him then and there. Instead, he turned Him over to his soldiers to be scourged. Perhaps he thought this would satisfy the mob and stop them from calling for His death.

Scourging was a terrible punishment. It was done with a whip that was brought down with great force on a prisoner's naked back. Poor Jesus! How He must have suffered as lash after lash fell upon Him! But it was not only the whip that hurt so much but the thought that men could be so cruel, unjust, and hateful.

Soon His flesh was cut to ribbons and blood was flowing down His legs. Yet even this did not satisfy the beasts who were torturing Him. Some of them made a crown from pieces of a thornbush and shoved it down on Jesus' head. The sharp thorns opened up more wounds, and soon blood was flowing down His neck and cheeks.

After they had done their worst the soldiers put a purple robe on their bleeding prisoner and led Him back to the judgment hall.

When Pilate saw Jesus he turned to the crowd and cried, "Behold the man!"

"Crucify Him, crucify Him!" they yelled.

"Shall I crucify your King?" asked Pilate.

"We have no king but Caesar," roared the crowd. "If you release this man, you are not Caesar's friend."

At this Pilate gave in. Calling for a basin of water, he washed his hands, saying, "I am innocent of the blood of this just person: see ye to it."

But he wasn't innocent, and no water could ever wash away his guilt. He could have saved Jesus, but he didn't.

Now he gave the order for Jesus to be crucified, "and the soldiers led Him away."

"Hail, King of the Jews!" they sneered, as they took the purple robe off Him and dressed Him in His own clothes. But He took no notice of them.

Half dead from weariness, pain, and loss of blood, Jesus was now told to carry the great wooden cross on which He was to die. But it was too much for Him. He staggered under its weight.

Sure that their prisoner would never be able to carry such a load all the way to the place of crucifixion, the Roman soldiers wondered what to do next. Looking around at the people who had gathered to see the procession start, they picked on a strong-looking man and pressed him into service. He turned out to be Simon of Cyrene, a town on the north coast of Africa. He had just arrived in Jerusalem on a visit and now found himself ordered to carry a criminal's cross.

At first, probably, he was much annoyed at being told to do such a menial task; but years later how glad he must have been that he, an African, had been chosen for so great an honor!

The Bible says that Simon of Cyrene was the "father of Alexander and Rufus," and I've often wondered why these two boys are mentioned in the Holy Scriptures. Could it be because of what carrying the cross did for their father and for them? Anyway, I am sure that, ever after, they never stopped talking about their father's good fortune.

Someday you and I may be asked to carry a cross for Jesus. It may be heavy or light. But whatever it is, let us carry it cheerfully. When we meet Jesus in His kingdom we shall be so happy for everything—even the simplest errand—we have done for Him.

STORY 3

Nailed to a Cross

NOW THE procession is on the move again, with Jesus walking a little ahead of Simon of Cyrene, who is carrying the cross. The King of sufferers looks pale and worn but very brave. His head is "bloody, but unbowed."

Roman soldiers in bright armor and with spears in their hands march on either side, while behind follow hundreds of friends and enemies, "a great company of people, and of women," many of them weeping piteously and sobbing aloud.

By this time word has spread like wildfire through Jerusalem that Jesus of Nazareth, the beloved Teacher of Galilee, has been arrested and condemned to death.

The whole city is shocked. People can hardly believe their ears. "What a shame!" some cry. "How could they do such a thing to such a nice, kind man!"

More and more people start running toward the route they know He must follow as He goes to His death. The thou-

sands who have gathered for the Passover begin moving in the same direction. Soon the streets are lined with men, women, and children, all eager to catch one last glimpse of this strange and wonderful Person, now doomed to die.

And there He is! He said He was a king and He looks like a king, though His crown is made of thorns. See! He is trying His best to smile through all the cuts and bruises on His face. Now He's waving at some boys and girls on the roadside as they try hard to keep from crying. They were with Him in the Temple only a day or two ago singing, "Hosanna to the Son of David!"

He knows how hard it is for them to understand why He is letting Himself be killed. All He can do now is to let them see that the Son of David is no coward. He can take the worst that His enemies can do to Him without flinching.

Did He not say, only last Thursday night, "In the world ye shall have tribulation: but be of good cheer; I have overcome the world"? Now He is proving it is true. You can see it on His face. He is going to His death a conqueror.

Now the procession has stopped, soldiers and all. Jesus is talking quietly to a group of weeping women.

106

NAILED TO A CROSS

"Daughters of Jerusalem," He is saying to them, "weep not for Me, but weep for yourselves, and for your children." Gently He warns them of the dreadful things about to come upon their city as a punishment for all its sins. He speaks but a few words, but how brave they are! They tell of the courage in His heart, His certainty that His cause will win at last. What a man! What a God!

The procession winds through the city gate and up the rough, rockstrewn path to Calvary, "the place of a skull," where for centuries the worst criminals have been put to death by the fearful torture of crucifixion.

The soldiers are undressing Jesus now, taking off His robe and tossing it aside. Meekly He lies down upon the cross and stretches out His arms. A soldier comes up with a hammer and a bag of nails. He seizes one of the hands that so often touched the sick and made them well. As he starts to drive a nail through it into the cross, he looks at Jesus, wondering why he hears no cry of pain.

He stops hammering and listens. Jesus is saying something. It is scarcely more than a whisper but this pagan soldier has never before heard the like from the lips of a dying criminal.

"Father, forgive them; for they know not what they do."

It is the same when the second nail goes in. "Father, forgive them; for they know not what they do."

Even when the soldier drives the nails through His feet

there is still no word of complaint. No curse, no cry of harsh rebuke, no shout of vengeance. Nothing but the same tender whispering: "Father, forgive them; for they know not what they do."

The original Greek words suggest that Jesus not only said this once but *kept on saying it,* over and over again. So it became one of the great messages of the cross: "Forgive!" "Forgive!" "Forgive!"

How wonderful it would be if you and I could have this same beautiful spirit in our hearts when things go wrong and people find fault with us and do us harm! Next time you think that somebody at home or at school has been unkind to you, try to say, as Jesus did, "Father, forgive them; for they know not what they do." In forgiving you will both keep your heart at peace and win your enemy's friendship.

Now the soldiers are lifting the cross with its precious burden. There must be four or five men on the job. They guide it to a hole in the ground and drop it in. The jar on the Saviour's outstretched arms must be terrible. Still Jesus says nothing but "Father, forgive them."

Notice that sign above His head. Pilate ordered it to be placed there. It reads, in Hebrew, Greek, and Latin, "THE KING OF THE JEWS." The priests asked him to change it and make it read, "He said, I am King of the Jews," but Pilate wouldn't do it.

"What I have written I have written," he said. So it came about that the same Roman governor who sent Jesus to His death told the whole world who He really was.

108

NAILED TO A CROSS

Slowly, in great agony, Jesus is dying. The crowd draws near to watch the end.

"And sitting down they watched Him there."

The soldiers watch as they gamble for His garments.

The priests watch as they gloat over the victory they think they have won.

The women who followed Him watch through tear-dimmed eyes.

People whom He once healed of sickness watch with bowed heads and sorrowful hearts.

There are children watching too. There's a couple of them over there holding on to their parents as they look up at the cross with tears rolling down their cheeks. Mingled in the crowd are other boys and girls wishing with all their hearts that they could do something to help Him.

"Poor Jesus!" I can hear them saying. "He was so kind to us. He told us such lovely stories. Why, oh, why, did He have to die like this?"

Nobody answers. Nobody seems to know.

But there is an answer.

> "He died that we might be forgiven,
>   He died to make us good,
>   That we might go at last to heaven,
>   Saved by His precious blood."

STORY 4

Promise to a Thief

THREE crosses, not one, were raised on Calvary's hill that dreadful day. Two thieves were crucified with Jesus, one on His right, the other on His left.

Who they were, or where they were born, or what wrong they had done, we do not know. The Bible doesn't even mention their names. They were just two poor, very miserable men suffering and dying with the Son of God.

How old were they? We don't know that either. Most likely they were no older than Jesus, and He was only thirty-three. They may have been much younger.

Today such wrongdoers would be put in a reform school. In those days they were crucified. So different are the times in which we live, thanks to the Man on the middle cross.

I like to think of those two thieves as just two boys who went wrong—boys whose mothers loved them and had high hopes for them and were broken-hearted when they began to lie and steal.

PROMISE TO A THIEF

There must have been a moment in the lives of both of them when they left the path of goodness and started on the road that led them to dishonor and death. It may have been when they were talking with bad companions, or when they were first tempted to steal, but whenever it was, that word, that deed, that evil thought, was the beginning of their wrongdoing and of all their sorrows.

Step by step—maybe very slowly at first—they plunged deeper and deeper into sin.

Though, no doubt, brought up to believe in the Ten Commandments, they forgot all about them. Though they knew perfectly well that God had said, "Thou shalt not steal," they stole, right and left. Then came arrest and the sentence of death.

Finally the dreaded moment came. Carrying their crosses, the prisoners were led to the place of execution. Perhaps they were surprised to see another cross raised between theirs. Cer-

tainly they were amazed when they saw *who* was crucified there. They knew Jesus well. They had heard much about Him. Now in their awful agony they looked at Him, wondering.

Naked, His hands and feet nailed to the wooden beams, His face drawn and haggard, with blood still running down His forehead from the crown of thorns, Jesus did not look like one who could help them. Yet there was a majesty in His bearing, even on the cross.

Then "one of the malefactors which were hanged railed on Him, saying, If Thou be Christ, save Thyself and us."

This was no plea for help. It was a taunt, and a most unkind one at such a moment. This thief had no faith that the man on the middle cross was the Son of God. He was

merely mocking Him, repeating the words of the sneering priests below.

Then something beautiful happened—the one gracious deed that lighted the awful darkness and misery of that crucifixion scene. Turning on the first thief, the second thief rebuked him, saying: "Dost thou not fear God, seeing thou art in the same condemnation? And we indeed justly; for we receive the due reward of our deeds: but this man hath done nothing amiss."

How the heart of Jesus must have thrilled as He heard these words and knew that He had one champion left! Most of His disciples had forsaken Him and fled. Despite all He had done for the multitudes, healing the sick and raising the dead,

115

it looked just then as though he hadn't a friend left. Day after day, night after night, He had poured out His love for the needy and the sorrowing, but now all His labor seemed to have been in vain. Nobody loved Him—nobody, that is, except, oh, wonder of wonders, this dying thief! Though racked with pain, this poor sinner would not let an unkind, unjust word be said about Him! He was willing to admit his own sins, but would not let anyone accuse the innocent Teacher of Galilee.

Then it was that the repentant thief said, "Lord, remember me when Thou comest into Thy kingdom."

Again the heart of Jesus was deeply touched. Why, this poor thief not only believed that He was innocent, he believed that He was a king, and that beyond this dreadful death on the cross He would have a kingdom and life everlasting. In his simple way this thief had more true faith in Jesus and His mission than all His disciples put together!

If ever there was a man truly sorry for his sins, and sincerely longing to be a child of God, it was this poor dying thief. Surely no one ever was more deserving of a place in His kingdom. No wonder Jesus said to him: "Verily I say unto thee this day: with Me shalt thou be in Paradise."

This promise to the repentant thief is one of the most precious in all the Bible. "Today," said Jesus, in other words, "today, this darkest of days, when My cause seems lost, when most of My friends have left Me, and My enemies have crucified Me—today I tell you, victory is Mine, and you shall have part in it. The future is Mine, and you shall share it with Me."

PROMISE TO A THIEF

Jesus did not, as some think, tell the poor thief that he would be in Paradise that very day. He could not have meant that, for He did not go to Paradise Himself that day. Three days later, after His resurrection, He said to Mary, "I am not yet ascended to My Father." No. When Jesus spoke that precious promise to the dying thief, He was looking into the future, to the day of His final triumph, when all who love Him and are faithful to Him will be gathered into His kingdom.

"Lord, remember me," said the dying thief.

Will Jesus remember him? Indeed He will! Though a thousand million years should pass, Jesus would not, could not, forget this man who stood by Him in that dark and bitter day. If there is one person who is absolutely sure of a place in Paradise, it is the converted thief who, in his dying moments, turned to Jesus with all his heart, reached out by faith from cross to cross, and in reaching won heaven for himself.

STORY 5

"Good-by, Mother!"

I T IS now between twelve and three in the afternoon. A strange darkness is falling over the countryside, getting denser every moment, as though the light of the world is going out.

People become frightened. Some leave and go home. Those who remain huddle together, peering through the gloom at the three crosses on the hill.

Most of the noise has died down, giving place to silence.

At first, right after Jesus' cross had been raised, the priests and rulers had looked up at Him and sneered, "He saved others; let Him save Himself, if He be Christ, the chosen of God."

Others had passed by wagging their heads and saying, "Aha! You who would destroy the Temple and build it in three days, save yourself and come down from the cross."

Tauntingly the chief priests had said, "Let the Christ, the King of Israel, come down from the cross, that we may see and believe."

118

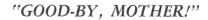

"GOOD-BY, MOTHER!"

Jesus had not replied. Nor had He come down from the cross. Even if He had, they wouldn't have believed in Him. They would still have found excuses for not believing, and doubtless they would have crucified Him again.

Now all is quiet. Even the soldiers are not talking much, having divided Jesus' clothes among them and cast lots for His seamless robe.

Somewhere, in the dark of this awful afternoon, several women are weeping their hearts out. Among the group is Mary, the mother of Jesus, "and his mother's sister, Mary the wife of Cleophas, and Mary Magdalene."

To all of them this is the saddest day of their lives, but Mary, the mother of Jesus, is hurt worst of all.

She had expected so much of Him—right from that wonderful moment when Gabriel had appeared to her and said, "Behold, thou shalt . . . bring forth a son, and shalt call His name Jesus. He shall be great, and shall be called the Son of the Highest: and the Lord God shall give unto Him the throne of His father David."

How high her hopes had risen at that moment! What dreams of glory had flashed through her mind! And now this!

Is this cross His promised throne? Is this all that God is going to do for Him?

She remembers Bethlehem, and the story the shepherds had told her of the angels who had appeared to them in a blaze of light, singing, "Glory to God in the highest," and of the one who had said to them: "Unto you is born this day in the city of David a Saviour, which is Christ the Lord." What a thrill of happiness these words had brought to her as she lay with her Babe in the stable! But now, could *this* be the fulfillment of that promise? How could He save anybody, hanging on a cross, dying a criminal's death?

She remembers what old Simeon said to her in the Temple as he took Jesus in his arms: "Behold this child is set for the fall and rising again of many in Israel; . . . (yea, a sword shall pierce through thy own soul also)." Could this cross be the sword?

Then, as she bows her head in misery, she thinks of those lovely, carefree days in dear old Nazareth. What a dear, sweet boy He had been! What a help about the house! How kind His nature; how gentle and loving His every thought and

deed! Surely He did not deserve this!

She thinks of His years of ministry, how
He tried to do so much for the poor, the sick,
the needy. Day and night He had worn Him-
self out for them. Always He had thought about others. Now
they had done this to Him. It wasn't fair! It wasn't right!

121

"GOOD-BY, MOTHER!"

Poor Jesus! How He must be suffering up there! Oh, if only she could do something, one little thing, to help Him, just to relieve His dreadful pain for one brief moment! But there is nothing, nothing she can do!

She peers up into His poor, wounded face. For a moment it seems that He is smiling at her. Yes! He is trying to speak to her. Eagerly she catches the whispered words.

"Woman," He says, "behold thy son!"

It is as if He had said, "Good-by, Mother. John will look after you." She cries again at the thought of His tender love.

Then His eyes turn to John—dear, faithful John—who is standing beside her. "John," He says, "behold thy mother!"

Did ever more beautiful words come from dying lips? Oh, wonderful, wonderful Jesus! In His last agonies He thinks about His mother!

Too weary, too racked with pain, to say more than these few words, He says enough for both to understand.

"And from that hour that disciple took her unto his own home"—a kindness that Jesus will surely repay ten thousand fold when He shall reward His own.

Do you love your mother as much as this? If you were in great trouble, would your last thought be for her and her welfare? I hope so.

You may never have to leave your mother for somebody else to look after as Jesus did; but you never know.

Sometime you may have to say, "Good-by, Mother," and never see her again. So love her and care for her the best you can today.

123

Mary, the mother of Jesus, her heart torn with grief, was the last one at the cross. Kneeling beside the disciple John she heard Jesus' whispered words asking him to care for her.

STORY 6

History Breaks in Two

IT IS now almost three o'clock—the ninth hour—the time for the slaying of the evening sacrifice in the Temple. On the hill of Calvary the Lamb of God is about to offer Himself a sacrifice for the sins of the world.

The darkness about the cross is now so dense that the dying Man upon it can scarcely be seen. Nature seems to be trying to hide the sufferings of its Creator.

Suddenly a voice rings out through the darkness crying, "Eli, Eli, lama sabachthani?" meaning, "My God, my God, why hast Thou forsaken Me?"

People still waiting by the cross look at one another and ask, "Did you hear Him? What does He want?"

Some think He is calling for Elijah. "Let us see whether Elijah will come to save Him," they say. But of course Jesus isn't asking for Elijah. He is crying out the agony of His broken heart.

This is the moment of Jesus' greatest suffering. Not only

124

is the torture of crucifixion at its worst, but the whole awful weight of the sins of all mankind is pressing down upon His soul. He thinks God must have forsaken Him. He feels cut off from His Father's presence.

Now He speaks again. In a loud voice He cries, "It is finished!" "Father, into Thy hands I commend My spirit."

His head falls forward on His chest. He is dead.

The struggle is over; the victory is won. The price has been paid for man's redemption.

Jesus has done what He came to do. He has opened the way into the kingdom of God for all who believe in Him. He has kept the promise He made to Adam and Eve after they had sinned. He has made certain that the head of Satan, the wicked serpent, shall be crushed and that someday the earth shall be like Eden once again.

As we look at that poor dead figure upon the cross it seems that He has been defeated and all His plans have failed. But no. He has merely made possible a glorious victory over all evil.

Suddenly, as Jesus becomes limp and lifeless on the cross, all nature is convulsed. There is a fearful earthquake. Great rocks are split from the mountainside and go rolling down into the valley. Lightning flashes. Thunder roars. The elements seem to cry out in fury at the wicked deed that has been done.

Panic seizes the crowd about the cross. Priests and people flee for their lives, sure that the judgments of heaven are about to burst upon them.

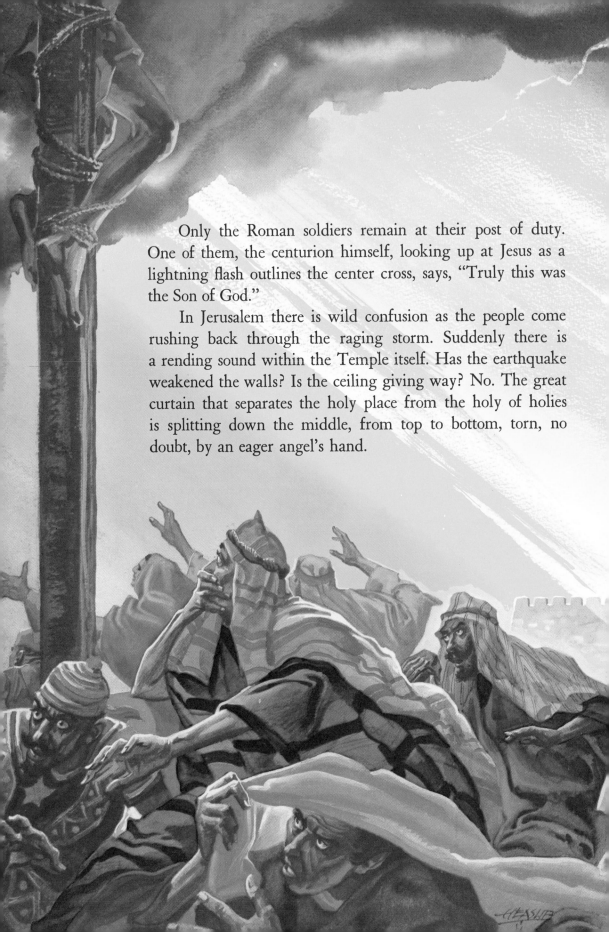

Only the Roman soldiers remain at their post of duty. One of them, the centurion himself, looking up at Jesus as a lightning flash outlines the center cross, says, "Truly this was the Son of God."

In Jerusalem there is wild confusion as the people come rushing back through the raging storm. Suddenly there is a rending sound within the Temple itself. Has the earthquake weakened the walls? Is the ceiling giving way? No. The great curtain that separates the holy place from the holy of holies is splitting down the middle, from top to bottom, torn, no doubt, by an eager angel's hand.

PAINTING BY
WILLIAM HEASLIP

There is no need for it any longer. The Temple, the services, the sacrifices, have all served their purpose. The sacrifice of Jesus, to which they all pointed, has been made. Now all men, Jews and Gentiles, of all nations, kindreds, tongues and people, may come to God through Jesus, any time, anywhere, they will.

It is the dawn of a new day for the world.

The crucifixion of Jesus is the Great Divide in the history of mankind. From Eden everything moves up to it; after it everything moves on toward His return in glory.

His great sacrifice on Calvary tears history in two, so that people talk of B.C., before Christ; and A.D., after Christ (meaning *anno Domini,* "the year of our Lord").

Even the cross itself seems to point in both directions—one arm toward the past, the other toward the future—as if to tell us that the love of Jesus reaches out in loving invitation to every boy, every girl, every man, every woman, ever born upon the earth. Hanging there as the poor dead Lamb of God, the King of sufferers seems to say to one and all, "Look unto Me, and be ye saved, all the ends of the earth." That salvation means happiness here and life with Him forever.

STORY 7

The Man Who Pulled the Nails

THE KING of life was dead. He who but a few brief days before had called Lazarus from the tomb now hung limp and lifeless upon a cross. He who had brought health, strength, and happiness to thousands was now unable, it seemed, to help anyone any more.

The soldiers gathered at the foot of the cross couldn't believe that Jesus was already dead. Usually crucifixion took much longer to kill a man. So one of them raised his spear and stabbed Him in the side. From the jagged wound flowed "blood and water," clear proof of death.

John was standing there and saw this happen, and it reminded him of the words of the prophet Zechariah, "They shall look upon Me whom they have pierced."

Then he saw something else that made a cold shiver run down his back. Some important-looking Jews were talking with the soldiers and pointing up at the three crosses.

"You've got to get these men down before sunset," they

9-9

said. "We can't have them hanging there during the Sabbath, and the Passover Sabbath at that."

"Have you orders from Pilate?"

"Yes, we have. We have just been to him. He says they are to come down at once. Break their legs."

"As you say," said the soldiers. It didn't matter to them what happened. This was just one of the many ugly jobs they had to do.

Going over to one of the thieves, who was still groaning in agony, a soldier smashed his legs with a club. Then he went to the other thief—perhaps the one to whom Jesus had promised Paradise—and did the same.

Poor dying men! How they must have suffered!

Looking up at Jesus, the soldier saw He was already dead, and dropped his club. What was the use of breaking the legs of a corpse? This man would never run away. How little he knew of the future!

John breathed a sigh of relief. The very thought of his beloved Master's body being knocked about by a common soldier had sickened him. Then he remembered another prophecy, "A bone of Him shall not be broken." Back in the days of Moses, God had said that no bone of the Passover lamb must ever be broken.

And now John saw something else that surprised him no end and brought new courage to his heart.

A well-dressed man had joined the group at the foot of the cross. His noble bearing and rich robes told that he was a man of wealth and importance. Behind him

130

were his servants bearing ladders and a white linen shroud.

The man's name was Joseph of Arimathea, a member of the Sanhedrin. Good and just, he was one of the few who had not voted for Jesus to be put to death. He was, in fact, a secret disciple of the Master, looking "for the kingdom of God." The soldiers listened to him with respect.

"I have come for the body of Jesus of Nazareth," he said to the centurion. "Pilate has given me permission to bury Him."

"The governor has so informed me," said the centurion. "He has already checked to make sure that the Galilean is dead."

As servants hoisted a ladder against the cross, another kindly-looking gentleman approached. He, too, was well dressed and of noble appearance, and his servants bore a heavy jar of spices, "a mixture of myrrh and aloes, about an hundred pound weight." He was Nicodemus, another member of the Sanhedrin, the very one who had once come to Jesus by night and to whom the Master had said, "God so loved the world, that He gave His only begotten Son, that whosoever believeth in Him should not perish, but have everlasting life."

From then till now he too had been a secret disciple, believing in the teachings of Jesus, but afraid to let anybody know about it.

To John, who was still looking on, it must have seemed very wonderful that these two famous men should come forward in this dark, dark hour to pay their last respects to the poor dead Teacher of Galilee. Why had they done it? Could it be because they knew His disciples had not money enough to buy a tomb for Him or even to embalm Him properly? If so, how kind and thoughtful of them!

Now Joseph of Arimathea is climbing the ladder. (We know he went up himself, because the Bible says, "He took Him down.") He will not leave this precious task to anyone else. He comes to the pierced feet of Jesus. Leaning over, he grasps one of the nails with the powerful pincers the soldiers may well have lent him. He tugs at it. It comes out. He drops it and starts pulling on the other. This too yields and is dropped to the ground.

He moves the ladder over and climbs again, this time up to one of the outstretched arms. Joseph needs help. He calls Nicodemus, who climbs a second ladder to steady the body and keep it from falling. Now he seizes the nail that holds the hand to the wood and heaves on it with all his strength. It comes out. The arm falls.

One final pull and the last nail is out. The other hand is free. And now, very slowly, step by cautious step, these two grand old men bring Jesus gently down from the cross, perhaps with one limp arm around them, as though He were saying, "Thank you, friends, for coming; thank you for helping Me."

Secret disciples they may have been before. But never again! From this moment on their names would be known, loved, and honored all around the world.

And what a sweet thought it is that though someone who hated Jesus drove in those nails, someone who loved Him pulled them out!

133

← PAINTING BY HERBERT RUDEEN   © 1957, BY REVIEW AND HERALD

They were cruel hands of hate that nailed Jesus to the cross of Calvary, but the hands that took His body down and prepared it for burial were hands of tender love and sympathy.

STORY 8

The Creator Rests Again

WHILE all this was happening a sound of sobbing might have been heard from a large company of people, mostly women, who were standing some distance from the cross. They were the special friends of Jesus, many of them from Galilee, and they were heartbroken.

The Bible says that "all His acquaintance, and the women that followed him from Galilee, stood afar off, beholding these things."

Among those who were most sorrowful were "Mary Magdalene, and Mary the mother of James and Joses, and the mother of Zebedee's children." These had been very close to Jesus the past three years, and you can imagine how they were feeling now.

They had hoped and hoped, even up to the last minute, that Jesus would reveal His power and perhaps surprise everybody by leaping down unharmed from the cross.

134

THE CREATOR RESTS AGAIN

Hour after hour they had watched and waited in help-less misery. They had seen noon become dark as midnight. They had peered anxiously through the dense gloom at the three crosses on the hill. They had heard the last loud cry of their beloved Master. They had felt the earthquake and shuddered at the fearful lightning and the deafening peals of thunder. They had wondered whether these might be the heralds of His kingdom. But no. The storm had passed. The earth had ceased to shake. All was over. Jesus was dead. There was nothing to do but return to Jerusalem and try to forget.

It was almost sunset now, and the women knew they would have to go soon, but oh, how they hated to leave the spot! What would happen to His body after they had gone? they wondered. That it would be taken off the cross before the Sabbath they were sure, but what would the Romans do with it? Would they throw it into a criminal's grave, or leave it lying on the hillside for the crows and rats to devour?

Then someone saw the ladders.

"Look! They're going to take Him down!" a woman cried.

At this the whole company began to press nearer so that they might see better in the gathering dusk.

"Who is that pulling out the nails?" asked another.

"He looks like Joseph of Arimathea."

"It can't be! He's one of the richest men in Israel."

"But it is Joseph. I'm sure of it. And the man on the other ladder is Nicodemus."

Closer still they went to see this amazing sight.

"God bless them!" I can hear these women saying. "God bless them for being so brave and good to help our Master now!"

They watched as the two men gently lowered the body to the ground, covered it with the myrrh and aloes Nicodemus had brought, and wrapped it in the white linen shroud supplied by Joseph.

It was clear now that these two men planned to bury Jesus, but where?

Presently a little procession started winding down the hill. The women watched and wondered.

THE CREATOR RESTS AGAIN

Joseph and Nicodemus did not go far with their precious burden, for near the place where Jesus was crucified "there was a garden; and in the garden a new sepulchre, wherein was never man yet laid."

It was Joseph's own sepulcher, which he had built for himself and his family, no doubt at very great expense. If you ever go to Palestine you will be able to see it, or one just like it. I went inside it once and noticed how it was hewn out of solid rock, just as the Bible says—and how it was unfinished when Joseph gave it to Jesus.

Arriving at the tomb, Joseph and Nicodemus carried Jesus inside, laid Him gently upon the floor, and went out, closing the entrance by rolling a great stone across it. Then they went to their homes to keep the holy Sabbath.

So far as we know, no burial service of any kind was held for Jesus. There was no time. Since He died, as the Bible says, at "the ninth hour," or three o'clock in the afternoon, there were but three hours or so left till sunset, when the Sabbath began. During this time Joseph of Arimathea went to Pilate, Pilate sent for the centurion to find out whether Jesus was dead already, and later told Joseph he could have the body. Then Joseph walked, or rode on a donkey, to Calvary. He and Nicodemus took the body down, wrapped it in a shroud, and carried it slowly to the sepulcher.

Those were three busy hours, and it must have been very close to the Sabbath when the two men left for home.

As for the Galilean women, they left too, scattering to the tents they had put up for shelter during the Passover. The Bible says, "They returned, and prepared spices and ointments; and rested the sabbath day according to the commandment."

When all had gone, darkness and silence fell upon the sepulcher and the three crosses on Calvary's hill. The crowds that had thronged the place all day had disappeared.

Meanwhile in and around Jerusalem thousands of priests, rulers, scribes, Pharisees, Sadducees, and common people were piously observing the Sabbath, while the Lord of the Sabbath, whom they had just killed, rested in a lonely sepulcher outside the city walls.

Back in Eden, Jesus had rested on the seventh day after all His mighty works of creation. Now He was resting again on the seventh day at the close of His still greater and more glorious work of redemption.

STORY 9

Most Sacred Day

WHY DID the women from Galilee go to their tents and other lodging places "to prepare spices and ointments" when Nicodemus had already put a whole hundred pounds of myrrh and aloes around the body of Jesus? It could be that they hadn't seen him do it, or possibly they felt that the burial had been so hurried that a proper embalming should be done later.

The most interesting part of this story, however, is the fact that, much as they loved Jesus, these good women made no attempt to work on His body on the Sabbath.

Had they wished, they could have gone into the sepulcher right after Joseph and Nicodemus had left. No doubt they could have found someone to roll away the stone for them if they had tried hard enough. But they didn't do it.

They had all sorts of good excuses to do the task then and there. They could have reasoned that there was nothing more important in all the world at that moment than to give their

139

Master the burial He deserved. Had not Jesus told them that "it is lawful to do well on the sabbath days"? Had He not Himself healed the sick and done many wonderful deeds on the Sabbath? Had He not said that "the sabbath was made for man, and not man for the sabbath"? He had. And still they didn't do it.

Why? Because Jesus had never once told His disciples to do any unnecessary work during the sacred Sabbath hours.

After living with Jesus for three and a half years, the disciples knew just how He felt about the fourth commandment and Sabbathkeeping. They had no question in their minds as to which day they should keep, or how they should keep it. So, because the embalming of the body of Jesus was not absolutely necessary just then, they left the task undone, returned to Jerusalem, and waited for the holy hours of the Sabbath to pass.

And what a very sad Sabbath that was! The disciples were in despair. Some had already started back to Galilee. The rest were in hiding in and around Jerusalem, afraid that, now Jesus was dead, the priests and rulers would try to kill them also.

It was hard to believe that only this very week Jesus had ridden into Jerusalem at the head of a great procession of happy people, with some of them spreading palm branches before Him and children crying out, "Hosanna to the son of David: Blessed is He that cometh in the name of the Lord." As late as Thursday morning many still had hoped that He would take over the government of Israel and let Himself be crowned king. Eagerly they had waited for Him to reveal His power in some wonderful way, so that everyone would welcome Him as the long-hoped-for Messiah.

Instead, within twenty-four hours, Jesus had been arrested, tried, condemned, crucified! So suddenly had it all taken place that some could hardly believe it had really happened. It was as if the earth had opened up before them, and swallowed all their hopes. With Jesus gone, there was nothing left to live for. What *would* they do without Him? What *could* they do?

In little groups they talked of the beautiful life Jesus had lived among them, of the wise things He had said, of the kind deeds He had done, of the gracious and gentlemanly way He had always behaved, even to His enemies. How they had loved Him! How they would miss Him!

On Sabbath morning word spread among the disciples that the priests and rulers had learned where Jesus had been buried and had gone to Pilate, urging that a guard of Roman soldiers be placed around the sepulcher.

The rumor was true. A delegation had gone to the governor and said, "Sir, we remember that that deceiver said, while He was yet alive, After three days I will rise again. Command therefore that the sepulchre be made sure until the

third day, lest His disciples come by night, and steal Him away, and say unto the people, He is risen from the dead: so the last error shall be worse than the first."

Pilate had granted the request, saying, "Ye have a watch: go your way, make it as sure as ye can. So they went, and made the sepulchre sure, sealing the stone, and setting a watch."

As this news reached the women from Galilee they were plunged into still deeper sorrow. Now what could they do? They had planned to go to the tomb after Sabbath to embalm their Lord's body. Now this might be denied them. Would the soldiers let them by?

Slowly the hours of this saddest of all Sabbaths passed by. When at last sunset came again, it found the disciples still mourning for their Master. They could think of nothing but the fact that their beloved Jesus was dead and buried. To make matters worse, a hundred Roman soldiers were now guarding His body and a Roman seal was upon His sepulcher.

STORY 10

Most Awful Night

IF YOU had been in Jerusalem on that Saturday night after the crucifixion of Jesus, you would not have slept very much. I am sure the disciples didn't. They were too sorrowful, too disappointed, too worried, too afraid.

Right after sunset, when the Sabbath was over, many of them no doubt began to pack their things, ready to leave in the morning. Now that their Master had been put to death, they feared for their own lives. They were sure the priests and rulers would not stop until they rid Jerusalem of all His followers.

Others spent the night just talking about all that had happened during the past week. Over and over again they asked one another, with no hope of an answer, "Why did everything suddenly go wrong? Why did Jesus ride as a king into Jerusalem and then let Himself be crucified? Why did He bring Lazarus out of a tomb and then let Himself be buried in one? If He were indeed the Son of God, why did He not work a

miracle and come down from the cross in sight of everybody?"
It was all very hard to understand.

Slowly the night wore on. Midnight passed. Those who
had gone to bed fell into a troubled sleep. Those who had decided to sit up began to doze.

Suddenly there was a dull roar as the earth began to quake
and shudder again. Buildings trembled. Tents swayed. People
screamed. Dogs barked wildly. Men, women, and children,
half clothed, ran into the open, their faces pale with fright in
the starlight.

"An earthquake! Another earthquake!" they cried.

Out at the tomb where Jesus lay buried the quake seemed
to shake the whole mountain on which the crosses stood. The
Roman soldiers leaped to their feet in alarm. Some had been
sitting on boulders, while others lay on the ground half asleep,
waiting for the dawn. Now all of a sudden they were wide
awake, their eyes on the tomb they had been told to guard.

A moment later there was a brilliant burst of light that
seemed to fall from heaven to earth and envelop the tomb.
Then a dazzlingly beautiful being appeared from nowhere and
snapped the Roman seal, rolling back the great heavy stone as
though it had been a pebble.

"A spirit!" cried the soldiers, falling on their faces in
abject terror. They "became as dead men" the Bible says, so
frightened they were.

At that very moment Jesus, the King of life, strode forth
from His tomb in resurrection power and glory, and vanished
into the night.

144

MOST AWFUL NIGHT

When the light faded and the earth ceased to shake, the soldiers looked up again, only to find the tomb open and empty. Now a new fear seized them, for they knew Pilate would never forgive them for letting this happen, nor would he ever believe their story.

"We must tell the priests at once," some of them said. "They must help us or we are lost."

So they hurried into Jerusalem and, early though it was, demanded to see the chief priests at once.

Now the priests were scared. The earthquake had worried them enough, but the soldiers' report terrified them. What if it were true? What if Jesus of Nazareth had indeed risen from the dead as He had said He would? Such a story could rock the nation and turn the whole world upside down. There would be no end to the damage it would do to everything the priests stood for. It must be nipped in the bud.

So they called a special meeting of the Sanhedrin and repeated what the soldiers had told them.

All faces grew pale. This was terrible! They would have more trouble with this Galilean preacher now than before they crucified Him. All agreed that the story must be kept from the common people at all costs. Were it to get around among the thousands attending the Passover, there could be a riot.

But how could they stop the mouths of a hundred soldiers?

There was only one way—bribe them! So they added this sin to that of murder.

"Look," they said to the soldiers, "here's a large sum of money. It is yours if you agree to spread the rumor that His disciples came by night and stole Him away while you slept."

"But what about Pilate?" asked the soldiers. "Suppose he hears that we slept at our post of duty?"

"Never mind," said the priests. "Don't worry. We'll take care of that. If this comes to the governor's ears, we will persuade him, and secure you."

And that is what happened. The soldiers took the money and told the lie. To everybody who asked them what happened that night, they explained that the disciples came and stole the body of Jesus while they slept.

How many people believed them we shall never know, but the story was still being passed around many years later when Matthew wrote his Gospel.

And what a false and foolish story it was!

PART IV

Stories of the King of Life

(Matthew 28:1-20; Mark 16:1-20; Luke 24:1-53; John 20:1-21:25; Acts 1:1-11)

STORY 1

Most Glorious Morning

YOU CAN be sure that Mary, the mother of Jesus, and Mary Magdalene, and the mother of Zebedee's children, and the rest of the women from Galilee didn't sleep a wink that night. They had but one purpose in mind—to get back to the tomb as soon as possible and finish the task of embalming their Master's body.

Just how early they started out for the tomb nobody knows. Luke tells us that it was "very early"; John says that they got there "when it was yet dark"; and Matthew says that it was "as it began to dawn toward the first day of the week." Evidently it was a little while before sunrise.

In their trembling hands the women carried the spices they had begun to prepare before the Sabbath. They hoped that they might be able to persuade the guard to let them go into the tomb and embalm the body. Yet now, as they walked along the dark highway, a new worry troubled them. They remembered the stone that Joseph and Nicodemus had rolled in front

151

— PAINTING BY RUSSELL HARLAN   © 1957, BY REVIEW AND HERALD

Arriving at Joseph's tomb to complete the embalming of the body of Jesus, Mary was startled to hear the angel say who had rolled away the stone, "He is not here. He is risen."

of the sepulcher, a "very great" stone, much too heavy for
women to move. "And they said among themselves, Who shall
roll us away the stone from the door of the sepulchre?" At this
early hour, whom could they ask to help them?

Now they are picking their way over the rough land
near the place of burial. Suddenly they stop. Something has
happened. The tomb is open! The great stone no longer covers
the entrance. Someone has rolled it away!

They can hardly believe their eyes. What can this mean?
Has someone been here already and robbed the tomb of its
precious body? What of the guard? And the Roman seal?

They can see no soldiers. As for the seal, it is broken. Who
has dared to break this seal without permission from Pilate?

In the dim light of dawn they see an angel, not standing
by the tomb but sitting on the stone, as if to tell Pilate and the
whole Roman Empire who really rules the world. His face
shines "like lightning," and his raiment is "white as snow."

Very frightened, the women turn to flee from the scene,
but they are halted by the angel's lovely voice. "Fear not ye,"
he says, "for I know that ye seek Jesus, which was crucified.

152

He is not here: for He is risen, as He said. Come, see the place where the Lord lay."

The gentle invitation sets their fears at rest. They enter the sepulcher and find it empty, save for another beautiful angel sitting inside. The body of Jesus is nowhere to be seen. As they look around, searching for it, the angel says, "Why seek ye the living among the dead? He is not here, but is risen: remember how He spake unto you when He was yet in Galilee, saying, The Son of man must be delivered into the hands of sinful men, and be crucified, and the third day rise again."

"Go your way," the angel continues, "tell His disciples and Peter that He goeth before you into Galilee: there shall ye see Him, as He said unto you."

At this the women hurry from the sepulcher and head back to Jerusalem "with fear and great joy." Never have they run so fast in all their lives! What a story they have to tell!

Presently, panting and untidy, they reach the place where the leading disciples have been sitting out the night.

"We have just come from the tomb!" they cry. "It is empty! His body is not there! And we saw angels who said that He is alive!"

The disciples refuse to believe them. They think these poor women are so overtired and upset that they are "seeing things." Their words seem to them "as idle tales."

"But it's true, it's true!" they cry. "We saw the angels ourselves! They spoke to us. We heard them! One of them told us to tell Peter to meet Jesus in Galilee."

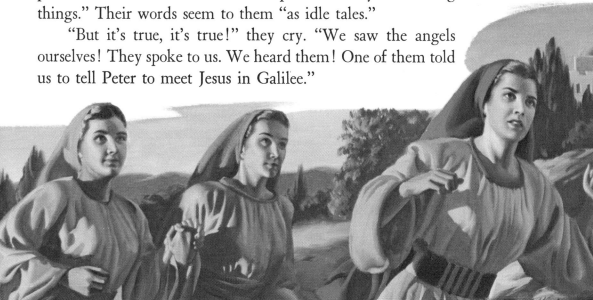

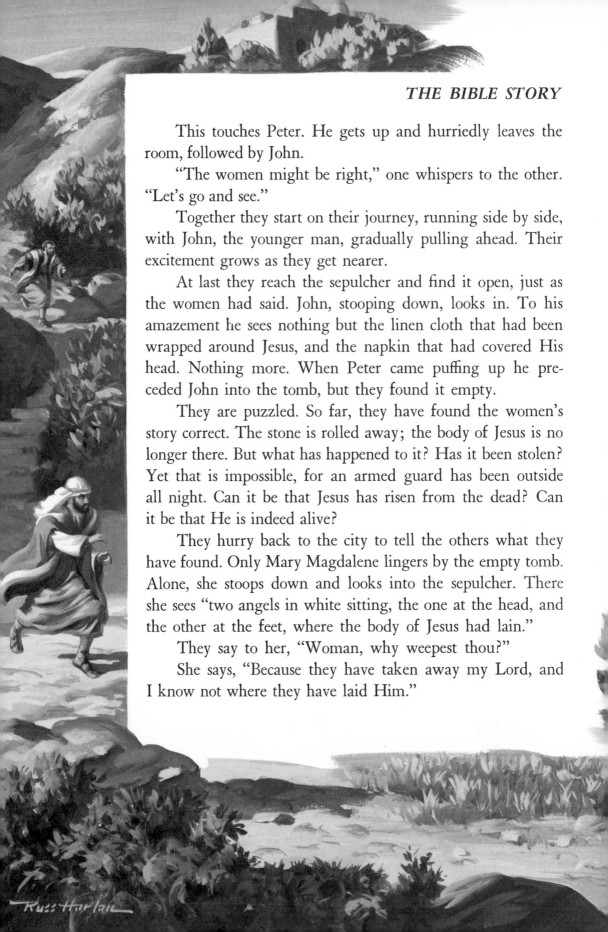

This touches Peter. He gets up and hurriedly leaves the room, followed by John.

"The women might be right," one whispers to the other. "Let's go and see."

Together they start on their journey, running side by side, with John, the younger man, gradually pulling ahead. Their excitement grows as they get nearer.

At last they reach the sepulcher and find it open, just as the women had said. John, stooping down, looks in. To his amazement he sees nothing but the linen cloth that had been wrapped around Jesus, and the napkin that had covered His head. Nothing more. When Peter came puffing up he preceded John into the tomb, but they found it empty.

They are puzzled. So far, they have found the women's story correct. The stone is rolled away; the body of Jesus is no longer there. But what has happened to it? Has it been stolen? Yet that is impossible, for an armed guard has been outside all night. Can it be that Jesus has risen from the dead? Can it be that He is indeed alive?

They hurry back to the city to tell the others what they have found. Only Mary Magdalene lingers by the empty tomb. Alone, she stoops down and looks into the sepulcher. There she sees "two angels in white sitting, the one at the head, and the other at the feet, where the body of Jesus had lain."

They say to her, "Woman, why weepest thou?"

She says, "Because they have taken away my Lord, and I know not where they have laid Him."

MOST GLORIOUS MORNING

Just then Mary looks around and sees someone standing near her. Supposing him to be the gardener, she says, "Sir, if thou have borne Him hence, tell me where thou hast laid Him, and I will take Him away."

Then the gardener speaks—God's Gardener. He says but one word: "Mary." It is enough. At once she recognizes Him.

"Master!" she cries, turning toward Him.

"Touch Me not," He says; "for I am not yet ascended to My Father: but go to My brethren, and say unto them, I ascend unto My Father, and your Father; and to My God, and your God."

Then He is gone. But Mary knows now that what the angels told her is true. She has seen Him herself! She has heard His voice! He is alive! He is risen from the dead!

As she rushes headlong to the city to tell the others the wonderful news, the sun is rising over the Jordan valley, bathing all the mountains round about Jerusalem with the light of a new day.

Another sun is shining too, for Jesus is risen, the Sun of Righteousness, whose warm and healing rays shall bless mankind through all the years to come.

Twin sunrise! Most glorious morning! Dawn of a great new day for all the children of men!

STORY 2

Mysterious Stranger

WHEN Mary Magdalene, panting and terribly excited, reached the place where many of the disciples were gathered, she felt sure they would believe her story. But they didn't.

"Now, now," I can hear them saying. "Calm yourself. You must have imagined it. You are just overtired. You couldn't have seen Him. It's impossible."

"But I *did* see Him!" cried Mary. "I did, I did!"

"Poor dear!" said someone. "You'll get over it."

"But He talked to me! He called me Mary! I would know His voice anywhere. And He told me He was going back to His Father in heaven. *Please* believe me!"

They didn't. They couldn't. Yet they were troubled by all the stories that were coming to them.

That the tomb was empty, there was no doubt. Peter and John had been there and found nothing but the linen shroud.

The body of their Master had disappeared in the night.

MYSTERIOUS STRANGER

That much was certain. Somebody had taken it. But who? And why?

Had the priests secretly buried it somewhere else so that the disciples would never find it? Had Pilate told the soldiers to get rid of it somehow to save any more trouble?

All day they talked, thinking up one explanation after another. There was nothing else they could do. Most of them were afraid to go outdoors lest they should be arrested. So they waited around, hoping things would quiet down enough for them all to slip out of town and be off to Galilee.

By and by two of them decided to risk it and go home. They were Cleopas and a friend, who lived at Emmaus, only eight miles from Jerusalem. Bidding farewell to the others, they started out. After passing through the city streets without trouble they were soon out on the main highway.

Their hearts were sad and their faces long. Everything had gone wrong. Both of them felt wretched and miserable. All their hopes had been built on Jesus, and now they had come tumbling down like a house of cards.

When they had seen Him riding into Jerusalem on that little colt they had felt sure He was about to proclaim Himself king of Israel. Instead, He had let Himself be arrested and put to death like a common criminal. It was just too bad.

What a good king He would have made! With His beautiful teachings about everybody loving everybody else, and with His wonderful power to heal the sick, His reign could have been the most glorious in Israel's history, far greater than David's or Solomon's. But now He was dead and buried. Well, He *had* been buried, but nobody knew where His body was. What a thing to happen! There was nothing to do but get back to work and try to forget it all.

As the two strode slowly on, deep in thought, they suddenly became aware that a stranger was walking beside them.

Surprised, they must have felt like asking, "Where did *you* come from?" but they were too courteous to say that. They just kept on walking.

The mysterious stranger spoke first. "What were you talking about just now that made you look so sad?" He asked.

Cleopas looked at Him. "Are you the only visitor to Jerusalem," he asked, "who does not know the things that have happened there in these days?"

"What things?" asked the stranger innocently.

"Concerning Jesus of Nazareth," said Cleopas, glad to tell the whole story to somebody who hadn't heard it before.

"This Jesus," he said, "was a prophet mighty in deed and word before God and all the people," but "our chief priests and rulers delivered Him up to be condemned to death, and crucified Him."

The stranger listened with deep interest.

"We had hoped," Cleopas went on, "that He was the One to redeem Israel. Yes, and besides all this, it is now the third day since this happened. Moreover, some women of our company amazed us. They were at the tomb early in the morning and did not find His body; and they came back saying that they had even seen a vision of angels, who said that He was alive. Some of those who were with us went to the tomb, and found it just as the women had said; but Him they did not see."

So Cleopas rambled on, telling everything he could remember of what had happened over the weekend.

Respectfully the stranger listened till he was through. Then, to the great surprise of both, He scolded them gently for being so ignorant!

"O foolish men," He said, "and slow of heart to believe all that the prophets have spoken! Was it not necessary that the Christ should suffer these things and enter into His glory?"

Then, though He had no Bible with Him, He quoted text after text from memory. "Beginning with Moses and all the prophets, He interpreted to them in all the scriptures the things concerning Himself."

What a wonderful Bible study that must have been! Seven whole miles of it, with the two disciples marveling at the amazing knowledge of their new-found friend.

As they drew near to Emmaus the stranger "made as though He would go further," but the others, who had enjoyed His company so much, would have none of it. "Stay with us," they urged Him, "for it is toward evening and the day is now far spent."

So the Stranger stayed for supper, and Cleopas asked Him to say grace, which He gladly did. Then it was, as "He took the bread and blessed, and broke it, and gave it to them," that they recognized the Saviour.

"Jesus! Master!" they cried. But He was gone. He had "vanished out of their sight."

So Mary Magdalene had been right! She had seen the Lord after all! He was indeed alive! Oh, wonderful news! They must tell the others right away!

≋

STORY 3

Burning Hearts

≋

FORGETTING their hunger and weariness, Cleopas and his friend dash from the table and start running back to Jerusalem.

Normally they would never start on such a trip as late as this. But what do they care about the gathering darkness, or possibly robbers, with such a story to tell?

There can be no strolling now. They run as fast as they can, stumbling over rocks, falling down, picking themselves up, and ever hurrying on. On, on to Jerusalem!

Running so hard, they have little breath for talking. But they do manage to scold themselves for not recognizing Jesus earlier.

"Did not our hearts burn within us?" they say, "while He talked to us on the road, while He opened to us the scriptures?"

How different are they now from the two men who set out for Emmaus but a few short hours before! From poor, sad, hopeless creatures, dragging their feet, they have been changed into men of faith and courage, their hearts aflame with a glorious message. Instead of fleeing in despair from their enemies, they are rushing back into the midst of them, eager to dare anything for their risen Lord.

Puffing and panting through the city gate, they hurry to the house where they left the disciples earlier that day. Thumping on the door, they demand admittance. Carefully someone opens it, peering anxiously into the night to make sure no enemy is there.

Through the open door Cleopas and his friend see a group of tense, excited people, one of whom, recognizing them, cries out, "The Lord is risen indeed, and has appeared to Simon!"

But the men from Emmaus have great news too, and they set out to tell it: how they met Jesus on the highway, how He

walked with them for two hours or more, and how they recognized Him as He broke bread at supper.

Everyone in the room is thrilled at this new proof that Jesus is alive. Surely, they say, it must be true He is risen from the dead.

Suddenly, as all are talking excitedly over this latest piece of news, someone cries out, "Look! There He is!"

All eyes turn toward the wonderful Person who has suddenly appeared in their midst. They hear Him say, "Peace be unto you." But there is no peace in their hearts. They are filled with fear, sure that this shining Being must be a ghost. But this is no ghost, or spirit; it is Jesus Himself.

"Why are you troubled?" He asks, "and why do questionings rise in your hearts? See My hands and My feet . . . ; for a spirit has not flesh and bones as you see that I have."

Then to their great surprise He says, "Have you anything here to eat?"

He *must* be real, then, if He is hungry, and wants to eat!

They scurry around, looking in the cupboards. There isn't much. Just a piece of cold broiled fish and part of a honeycomb. But they offer their last scraps to Him gladly, pleased to be able to do something for Him again.

Though King of life and Lord

163

of all creation, He accepts the simple food with grateful thanks. As He eats it everybody present watches Him with wide-open eyes.

The little meal over, Jesus begins to give these disciples the same Bible study He gave to Cleopas and his friend on the way to Emmaus. He opens their minds "to understand the scriptures," saying, "Thus it is written, that the Christ should suffer and on the third day rise from the dead, and that repentance and forgiveness of sins should be preached in His name to all nations, beginning from Jerusalem."

They love every word He says. Their sadness vanishes. New hope fills their hearts. Jesus is alive! He has come back from the dead! He has kept His promise! And the great prophecies He used to talk about are true after all!

Suddenly their hearts begin to burn too. The dying embers of their faith and courage leap into flame again. From a group of discouraged, defeated men they change into blazing champions of their beloved Lord, ready to tell His wonderful story to the ends of the earth.

≈≈≈≈≈≈≈≈≈

STORY 4

Why Thomas Doubted

≈≈≈≈≈≈≈≈≈≈≈≈≈≈≈≈≈≈≈

FOR SOME reason or other Thomas was not present when Jesus appeared among His disciples that Sunday evening. Possibly he had gone on an errand, or he may have been busy getting ready to return to Galilee. Anyhow, he was absent. And being absent he missed being among the first to see Jesus after His resurrection.

Just when he heard what had happened while he was away we do not know. It could have been that same night, or the next morning. But whenever it was, his friends were full of the exciting story and very eager to tell him about it.

"We have seen the Lord," they said. "He appeared to us. We saw Him and talked with Him. Now we know for sure that He is risen from the dead."

"Nonsense!" said Thomas. "You're just like the women. Seeing things. I don't believe it."

Day after day he refused to believe their story. Perhaps it was because he felt a bit left out. By this time he had heard

165

that Jesus had appeared to Mary Magdalene, to Peter, to Cleopas, and finally to all the disciples in the upper room. Why had He appeared to everybody else and not to him? It could be that a little bit of jealousy had added to his doubts.

In any case he decided he would not believe unless he himself actually saw Jesus. "Except I shall see in His hands the print of the nails, and put my finger into the print of the nails, and thrust my hand into His side," he said, "I will not believe."

All week long he held doggedly to this idea. Nobody could move him from it.

Some have thought that it was very wicked of Thomas to doubt so long, but they forget that all the disciples doubted at first. When they heard the stories that the women brought from the open tomb, they called them "idle tales." Thomas only doubted a few days longer than the rest.

And Thomas had many good points. He was a very brave man, and most devoted to Jesus during His ministry.

Now, not having seen Jesus since His crucifixion, he was in doubt. Out of loyalty to his beloved Master he did not want to make a mistake. Could the stories of His resurrection be true? He was not sure. "I'll believe when I see Him," he said to himself, "but not before."

All that week he worried about it. As the days went by, his doubts increased. If Jesus were alive, as the others said, why did He not appear again?

Another Sabbath came, one week after that saddest Sabbath in history, and still there was no sign of Jesus. Most of the disciples were now sure He was alive somewhere—but

166

where? Only one of the twelve seemed inclined to doubt.

"I can't believe He is alive," Thomas said to himself; "I won't believe it; not unless I see the print of the nails in His hands."

Sabbath passed, and Sunday too. It was now ten days since the crucifixion.

Then, in the evening, as the disciples were all together in the same upper room, "came Jesus, the doors being shut, and stood in the midst, and said, Peace be unto you."

This time Thomas was there with the rest, and what a look of blank surprise came over his face! He may well have felt ashamed, too, after all his doubting. For surely this was Jesus. There could be no question now. The others had been right all the time. The Lord had indeed risen from the dead.

Now Jesus was looking straight at him, right through him! That dear, familiar voice was calling him by name.

"Thomas," said Jesus, "reach hither thy finger, and behold

My hands; and reach hither thy hand, and thrust it into My side: and be not faithless, but believing."

So Jesus had read his thoughts! Jesus had known all about his doubts! Jesus had heard every word he had said about touching the wounds in His hands and feet and side!

He did not want to touch them now. There was no need. Beyond all question this was the dear Master Himself. Kneeling humbly at His feet, he cried, "My Lord and my God!"

Then Jesus said to him, so kindly and gently, "Because thou hast seen Me, thou hast believed: blessed are they that have not seen, and yet have believed."

At that moment Jesus was thinking not only of Thomas but of many other people, all the people who should live from that day to this. He was thinking of all the boys and girls who would hear of Him through the years to come, and who would have to believe in Him without seeing Him. Blessed, He said, will they be.

This blessing is for you and for me, for nobody alive today has ever seen Jesus. Nobody can see Him—now. Yet we may believe in Him. Patriarchs, prophets, and apostles have told us all we need to know about Him. They have made Him so real that we can feel Him close by us, "closer . . . than breathing; nearer than hands and feet."

But, best of all, we have the word of Thomas, the man who doubted so much and then believed with all his heart. His story is written in the Bible so that you and I, not seeing, but believing, might fall on our knees before our beloved Jesus, saying, "My Lord and my God!"

STORY 5

Back to the Boats

B Y THIS time the Passover ceremonies were ended for another year. Thousands of people were streaming out of Jerusalem, eager to get back to their homes.

All were chattering excitedly. Never had they had so much to talk about.

Though the priests had hoped to get rid of Jesus of Nazareth by crucifying Him, His name was now on everybody's lips. Some talked about the way He had overturned the tables of the money-changers in the Temple; others about His trial and the grim procession to Calvary; others of the darkness at the cross and His last loud cry of agony. But the story that gripped all hearts was the one about the empty tomb. Here was a mystery of the first order. Who had taken His body? The priests, the soldiers, or the disciples? What had been done with it, and why?

While everybody was arguing this way and that, the rumor flew along every highway out of Jerusalem that Jesus wasn't dead after all. He had actually walked out of His own tomb at the time of the great earthquake!

Was the rumor true? Nobody could say. But on and on it went, the most exciting rumor in a thousand years.

As for the disciples, they were glad to be going back to Galilee, and they couldn't get there fast enough. Had not Jesus told them that He would meet them there?

Seven of them walked the whole way together—Peter, James, John, Thomas, Nathanael, and two others. All were pleased to be leaving the memories of Jerusalem behind them.

It was terribly lonesome without Jesus. The last time they had traveled this road—not many days ago—He had been with them, their Leader, their Teacher, and their Friend. Now they were on their own.

By this time, of course, they were quite sure He had risen from the dead, but they wished He might have been one of their little company, talking with them as of old.

On their journey they passed many a place that reminded them of Him. Every now and then one of them would say, "This is where He healed a leper," or, "This is where He gave a blind man sight," or, "It was here He told us that He came not to destroy men's lives but to save them."

When they reached Cana of Galilee a whole flood of memories crowded into their minds, for it was in this village that He had performed His first miracle at the marriage feast.

By and by they came to the brow of a hill from which they could see the lake they loved so dearly. It was beautiful as ever, so calm, so peaceful, and quite unchanged by all that had happened.

Eagerly they hurried down the last long hill to Tiberias, then on to Capernaum. How wonderful it was to be home once more!

Now their minds turned to the question of what to do next. Peter settled it for them all.

"I'm going fishing," he said.

"We'll go with you," said the others.

So they found their way to the old wharf, and there, to their joy, were the dear old boats, just as they had left them. What a thrill they got looking them over, bailing out the water, finding the oars, and getting the nets ready!

Those boats were so tempting that the seven disciples could hardly wait to get into one of them again. The Bible says, "They went forth, and entered into a ship immediately." I am sure they did. They couldn't help it.

I think I know how they felt. I have been on a boat on Galilee and seen fishermen haul in their nets loaded with fish. It was a wonderful feeling!

But a sad disappointment awaited the disciples that night. They couldn't catch any fish. Time after time they threw out

their nets and hauled them in, only to find them empty. It was very discouraging, especially as they badly needed the money that a good haul would bring them. I wouldn't be surprised if they said to one another, "We've forgotten how to do it. We've lost our skill all these months we've been away."

The stars came out, and still there were no fish. Midnight passed, and their nets were yet empty. Dawn began to break, and there was nothing to show for their night's toil.

As the morning light grew brighter they noticed a man standing on the shore.

"Who can that be standing there at this time of the morning?" one asked.

"Can't tell," said the others. "Seems to be a stranger in these parts."

Then to their surprise the stranger spoke to them, His voice carrying clearly across the hundred yards or so of water that separated them.

"Children, have you any fish?" He called.

"No," they said sadly.

Then to their amazement the stranger said, "Cast the net on the right side of the boat, and you will find some."

Should they, or shouldn't they? How could this stranger know where the fish were to be found? So near the shore, too. Who did he think he was, telling *them*? Had they not toiled all night and caught nothing?

But the stranger's voice was so friendly they couldn't take offense. After all, he might know something. They could try.

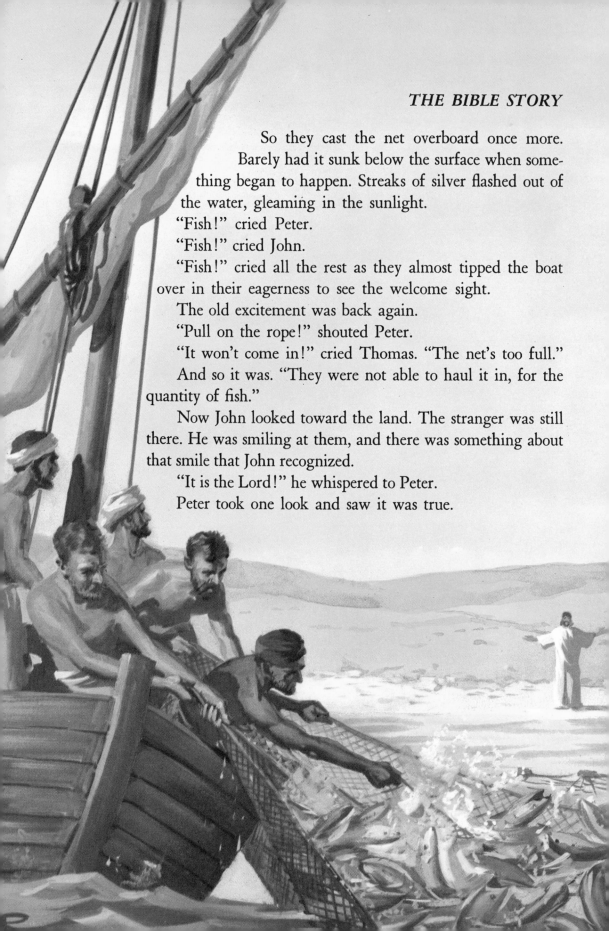

So they cast the net overboard once more. Barely had it sunk below the surface when something began to happen. Streaks of silver flashed out of the water, gleaming in the sunlight.

"Fish!" cried Peter.

"Fish!" cried John.

"Fish!" cried all the rest as they almost tipped the boat over in their eagerness to see the welcome sight.

The old excitement was back again.

"Pull on the rope!" shouted Peter.

"It won't come in!" cried Thomas. "The net's too full."

And so it was. "They were not able to haul it in, for the quantity of fish."

Now John looked toward the land. The stranger was still there. He was smiling at them, and there was something about that smile that John recognized.

"It is the Lord!" he whispered to Peter.

Peter took one look and saw it was true.

STORY 6

Breakfast by Galilee

IT WAS indeed Jesus, come to help them once more! How glad they were to see Him! He was worth more to them than ten thousand boatloads of fish.

Quickly putting on some clothes, "for he was stripped for work," Peter leaped into the water and waded ashore. The rest followed in the boat, dragging the netful of fish behind them.

I wish John had told us all that happened next. Maybe he was so busy with the boat and the fish that he never saw the tears of joy running down Peter's cheeks as he fell on his knees and worshiped the Master he loved so dearly. Maybe he never heard Peter say, "O Jesus, my Lord, how good it is to see You again! Stay with us! Don't leave us any more!"

The others were crowding around now, all telling Him how happy they were to see Him. What a wonderful meeting that was!

Then they smelled something that made them feel good

all over. It was the welcome odor of broiling fish and toasting bread.

Then they saw it—a charcoal fire on the beach beside them, "with fish lying on it, and bread."

Suddenly the whole beautiful truth broke on their minds. Jesus had got their breakfast ready! Knowing how hungry they must be after their long, weary night on the lake, He had planned this lovely surprise for them. Though the Son of God and the risen Christ, He had brought along the charcoal and the bread and lighted the fire. Yes! And He may have gone fishing Himself before they got there, or else how were fish on that fire?

Jesus had known all along, too, that He didn't have enough fish for so many husky men, and that's why He told them where to throw the net.

Now He said to them, "Bring some of the fish you have just caught." So Peter and some of the others got back in the

176

boat and hauled in the netful of fish, which had been entirely forgotten in the joy and excitement of meeting Jesus again. They found it full of large fish, "a hundred and fifty-three of them."

Now, with plenty of food at hand, Jesus said to the seven of them, "Come and have breakfast."

He was the host "and took the bread and gave it to them, and so with the fish."

Beautiful, unforgettable scene! Jesus, the King of life, waiting on His poor, tired disciples, who had been up all night fishing. No wonder they loved Him! No wonder they were willing to do anything He asked of them, and to die for Him if need be!

And is there any more beautiful invitation in all the Bible than this, "Come and have breakfast"?

Truly there is the important invitation to Noah: "Come thou and all thy house into the ark."

There is the loving invitation to sinners: "Come now, and let us reason together, saith the Lord."

There is the tender invitation to the weary: "Come unto Me, all ye that labour and are heavy laden, and I will give you rest."

There is the urgent invitation to supper: "Come; for all things are now ready."

But surely the sweetest of all is this simple invitation to breakfast—an invitation that every boy and girl can understand. For we all love breakfast, don't we? Whatever would we do without it? It is the first meal of the day. In its strength we go forth to do our work and enjoy our play.

So it was then. That breakfast was the beginning of a great new experience for those disciples.

Their fishing days on Galilee were over forever. From now on they were to start on the great work for which Jesus had been preparing them so long.

That call to breakfast was the call to a new work and a new life for every one of them. From that day forth they were to "catch men" for the kingdom of God.

STORY 7

"Feed My Sheep"

AFTER that wonderful breakfast on the beach, while the other disciples were busy clearing up, Jesus had a last quiet talk with Peter.

"Simon," He said, pointing to the boat, the net, and the fish that were left, "do you love Me more than these?"

That was a hard question for a fisherman, but Peter was ready for it. He had made up his mind. He was willing to give up everything for Jesus now.

"Yes, Lord," he said; "you know that I love you."

"Feed My lambs," said Jesus.

There was deep meaning in these simple words. Jesus knew He would soon be going back to heaven. The Chief Shepherd would be leaving His precious flock in a cruel world, and He wanted Peter to help take care of it. He wanted this good fisherman to become a good shepherd and look upon all new disciples, and especially the boys and girls, as His own dear lambs. He was to treat them with kindness and gentleness, feeding them the truths of the Word in such a simple way that they would be able to understand them easily. He was not to make of himself a self-important overlord and order people about like an army officer. Instead, with the tenderness of a shepherd, he was to lead them gently in the way they should go.

By and by Jesus spoke again.

"Simon," He said a second time, "do you love Me?"

"Yes, Lord," said Peter; "You know that I love You."

"Tend My sheep," said Jesus.

He wanted Peter to see that if he loved Him truly, he must also love his fellow disciples and all others who would come to believe in Jesus in days to come. He must ever be thoughtful of their needs and shield them with his life from harm and danger.

Now for the third time Jesus asked, "Simon, . . . do you love Me?"

This upset Peter. The Bible says he was "grieved." He began to wonder if Jesus didn't believe him. Why had He asked the same question three times?

"Lord, You know everything," he replied; "You know that I love You."

It was a good answer, and Jesus loved him the more for saying it. He was sure now that Peter would be a good shepherd. And he was. In fact, Peter never forgot this last request Jesus made of him by the Sea of Galilee to feed His lambs and His sheep.

Nearly thirty years later, when he wrote his first epistle to the Gentile Christians in Asia Minor, Peter urged all church

pastors to be good shepherds too, an example to their flocks.

"Feed the flock of God which is among you," he said to them, "taking the oversight thereof, not by constraint, but willingly; not for filthy lucre, but of a ready mind; neither as being lords over God's heritage, but being ensamples to the flock. And when the Chief Shepherd shall appear, ye shall receive a crown of glory that fadeth not away."

But before Jesus bade farewell to Peter that lovely morning He said something else to him of great importance. Drawing back the curtain of the future for a moment, He let His faithful disciple see what loving Him would mean.

"When you were young," He said, "you girded yourself and walked where you would; but when you are old, you will stretch out your hands, and another will gird you and carry you where you do not wish to go."

Thus He let Peter know how he would die. Someday he too would be crucified, just like his Master.

And so it turned out during the terrible persecution of the church under the Roman emperor Nero. When the time came, however, so the story goes, Peter begged to be crucified upside down, because he felt unworthy to suffer exactly as Jesus had.

Strange it is, where love for Jesus will sometimes lead. Often it brings one into hardship and suffering. But though it may lead to a cross in this life, it will surely lead to a crown in the life to come.

When the Chief Shepherd shall appear He will fully reward His own. And the crowns He has in store for His faithful undershepherds will never fade through all eternity.

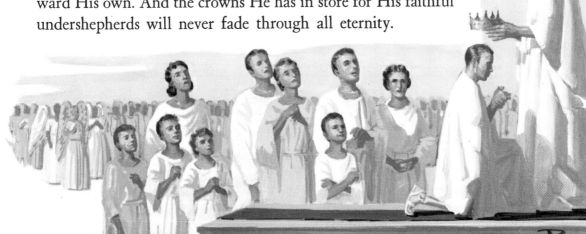

STORY 8

Forty Wonderful Days

BEFORE many days had passed, all Galilee knew that Jesus had appeared to seven of His disciples by the lake. The news spread like wildfire from village to village.

His many friends in Cana, Capernaum, Tiberias, Nazareth, and other places had been plunged into deep sorrow by His crucifixion, and you can imagine how startled they all were to learn that He wasn't dead after all. Though sealed in a tomb He had walked right out of it and was back in Galilee!

It was almost too wonderful to believe, but it was true. Seven people couldn't be mistaken. Had they not had breakfast with Him? Had not Peter, whom everybody trusted, had a long talk with Him about his future work?

Can't you hear the boys and girls talking about it all?

"It *must* have been Jesus," says one. "He was standing there on the beach, just as He used to do. And He told them where to cast their net and they caught more than 150 big fish."

"Yes," says another. "And He even lighted a fire and

started cooking before they got ashore. And He talked and smiled just as He always did before He died. I wish we could see Him too."

By and by the rumor spread that Jesus would meet His disciples again on the mountain where He had talked with them so many times before. Soon scores of men and women, boys and girls, were on their way there, all hoping that they would see Him and hear Him once more.

More and more people arrived until there were more than five hundred gathered at the old familiar meeting place. All were talking excitedly about the events of the past few weeks and guessing when and where Jesus would come among them.

Some were sure that this was the moment they had been waiting for so long when their beloved Master would declare Himself to be the king of Israel. If He could rise from the dead, surely He could drive the Romans out of the land, cleanse Jerusalem of its wickedness, and bring in the golden age all the prophets had talked about. Maybe He would even appear to them as a king, dressed in royal robes and with a beautiful crown on His head.

They were mistaken. Suddenly someone caught sight of a familiar figure walking toward the company along a mountain trail. He wore no crown or royal robes. Instead, He looked

just the same as when He had come to talk with them in the dear old days they remembered so well.

"It's Jesus!" they all cried. "It's the Lord Himself!" And the joy in their voices told Him how very welcome He was.

All five hundred saw Him at once. The Bible says so in 1 Corinthians 15:6. How could anyone doubt now that He had risen from the dead? Five hundred people couldn't be mistaken.

Then Jesus talked with them. Alas, we know but little of what He said. What a pity somebody didn't write it all down!

Only these few wonderful words remain of that last great sermon on the mount: "All power is given unto Me in heaven and in earth. Go ye therefore, and teach all nations, baptizing them in the name of the Father, and of the Son, and of the Holy Ghost: teaching them to observe all things whatsoever I have commanded you: and, lo, I am with you alway, even unto the end of the world."

There was much to be done yet before His kingdom could be set up on earth. True, He was their king; He had all power in heaven and in earth; but His kingdom would come through teaching, not through fighting.

And they could all help to make His plans work out. They must go to all nations, in all the wide, wide world, telling the story of God's love, persuading people to love one another, and preparing them to live happily in a kingdom of love forever and ever.

They would pass through trial, hardship, and disappoint-

ment, but they need not worry. He would be with them always, "even unto the end of the world."

Never would He forget them. Never. Not though a thousand years should pass. Always and always they would be dear to Him. There would not be a day, an hour, a single moment, when He would not be thinking of them in love.

As Jesus said, "Go ye therefore," each man present thought He was speaking to *him*. Each woman thought He was speaking to *her*. And so with the boys and girls. Each one said afterward, "He was talking to *me* and telling *me* to go. I know. He was looking straight at me." And of course He was. He wanted everybody who believed in Him to go and "preach the gospel to every creature."

"And these signs shall follow them that believe," added Jesus. "In My name shall they cast out devils; they shall speak with new tongues; they shall take up serpents; and if they drink any deadly thing, it shall not hurt them; they shall lay hands on the sick, and they shall recover."

What a promise! And all this power is for those who go and tell others the good tidings of His love.

This does not mean that we can pick up snakes just for the fun of it and expect them not to bite us. Nor does it mean that we can drink poison for a lark and it won't kill us. Of course not. But it does mean that we can go on God's errands, to do the work He has asked us to do, certain that He will take care of us. Many a miracle has He worked for those who have loved and served Him faithfully, and He will do the same for you if need be—if you love Him just as much.

How long Jesus stayed with His five hundred disciples on the mountain the Bible does not say, but we do know that He spent forty days with them after His resurrection, showing Himself to be alive by "many infallible proofs" and "speaking of the things pertaining to the kingdom of God."

Precious days! Wonderful days! How short they must have seemed! How soon they were over!

PAINTING BY ANDREW SEDLAC

STORY 9

Angels With a Promise

WHILE Jesus was in Galilee He must have told His eleven special friends to go to Jerusalem and wait for Him there. For the next time we hear of them they are in a room in the city—probably the same upper room where they ate the last supper together—and Jesus is "eating together with them" again.

Things are very different now. The cross is past. So is the resurrection. Jesus has died and risen again. He is alive forevermore. All power in heaven and earth is His, and no one can take it from Him.

But while Jesus is strong, His disciples are weak—far too weak for the great burdens they will have to carry when He has returned to heaven. So He urges them to wait in Jerusalem until they receive "the promise of the Father."

What is "the promise of the Father"? It is something the Father wants to give them because they have so faithfully followed His Son. It is something that will change them suddenly

187

from ordinary men—fishermen, taxgatherers, and the like—into mighty men of God, brave, tireless, powerful preachers of the gospel.

"John baptized with water," Jesus tells them, "but before many days you shall be baptized with the Holy Spirit."

Still thinking about the kingdom, they ask, "Lord, will You at this time restore the kingdom to Israel?"

"It is not for you to know times or seasons which the Father has fixed by His own authority," He answers. "But you shall receive power when the Holy Spirit has come upon you."

Will the coming of the Holy Spirit mean the setting up of the kingdom they have hoped for so long? No. The Holy

Spirit will bring them the strength, wisdom, and courage to preach the gospel of the kingdom to people who have never heard of it. "You shall be My witnesses in Jerusalem and in all Judea and Samaria and to the end of the earth."

Here was a new idea indeed. How could a little group of poor, humble, uneducated fisherfolk witness in the very city where the priests and rulers had put Jesus to death? And how could they, without money or possessions of any kind, carry the gospel to the "uttermost parts" of the earth? How could the Holy Spirit, "the promise of the Father," make such things possible?

Still wondering what Jesus could mean by these strange words, they walk with Him once more to the Mount of Olives. This time they do not stop at the Garden of Gethsemane, but climb on up to the top. Their pace is slow, for something tells them that He is going to leave them soon and they want to keep Him as long as they can.

Now Jesus is looking at them all with a special tenderness in His eyes. The hour of parting is at hand. He loves these dear men. Every one of them. He has lived with them for more than three years. He knows how much they have given up for Him and how much they will soon have to suffer as they witness in His name.

Dear Peter! Dear James! Dear, dear John! And Thomas, too, bless him, despite his doubts. And Matthew, Philip, and all the rest. Such good men and true, with all their faults!

"Bless you, bless you, every one!" I can hear Him saying, and there are tears in His voice.

Suddenly they notice that He is rising into the air. He is going away! Yes! Up, up, up, He goes, farther and farther, until at last a cloud receives Him out of their sight.

"Farewell!" they cry. "Farewell, dear Master!" Perhaps they wave their hands, then wipe their eyes.

He has disappeared; but still they look, peering into the depths of space, hoping against hope that they may catch one more glimpse of Him. But He has gone. Gone! And the dreadful thought comes to them that He may have gone for good. A desperate sadness fills their hearts.

Then of a sudden they notice two strangers standing near them, both dressed in white. Who can they be?

"Ye men of Galilee," say the strangers, "why stand ye gazing up into heaven? this same Jesus, which is taken up

from you into heaven, shall so come in like manner as ye have seen him go into heaven."

Now they know! These two men must be angels, sent by their beloved Master to comfort their hearts with the promise that someday He will come back again.

How kind, how thoughtful of Him! On His way to the glory land, with all the shining host of heaven around Him, He has remembered His friends left behind on earth!

They hurry back to Jerusalem "with great joy."

All sadness gone, they are "continually in the temple, praising and blessing God," so glad that "this same Jesus," their own Jesus, will return. How comforting is this "blessed hope"!

And what a beautiful hope it is, even today! "This same Jesus" is indeed coming again. The very same Jesus who healed the sick, raised the dead, loved the children, and told such beautiful stories is coming again. The same dear Jesus of Nazareth, Capernaum, and Cana, who did so many kind deeds for the poor and needy, who was always so gentle and gracious and good, is coming again.

It will not be another Jesus, a different Jesus, but "this same Jesus." Time will not have aged or altered Him, for He is "the same yesterday, and to day, and for ever." When He comes back down that shining pathway through the skies, it will be the same Jesus who went away, unchanged by the changing years. We shall know Him by the smile on His face, by the sweet melody of His voice, and by the marks of the nails in His hands.

192